JACOB STEINER, c. 1855(?)

THE SCRIPTA MATHEMATICA STUDIES

NUMBER FOUR

JACOB STEINER'S

Geometrical Constructions with a Ruler

Given a Fixed Circle with Its Center

Translated from the first German edition (1833) by

MARION ELIZABETH STARK

Professor of Mathematics, Wellesley College

Edited with an Introduction and Notes by

RAYMOND CLARE ARCHIBALD

Professor Emeritus of Mathematics, Brown University

Published by Scripta Mathematica • Yeshiva University • New York

1950

CONTENTS

EDITOR'S INTRODUCTION

I

IT IS more than a century since STEINER's famous little book on *Geometrical Constructions*, with a straight edge, was first published, and during that period there have been French (partial), Russian, and Polish translations of the work, as well as various German editions. That an English edition would be highly interesting and stimulating to numerous teachers and students in colleges and universities, and junior colleges, throughout the country can hardly be questioned. It must therefore be a source of great satisfaction to many mathematicians that Professor STARK has prepared such an admirable English text of STEINER's booklet. Here we have the first English translation of any work of STEINER. Although somewhat elementary in character, it is a good illustration of the effervescence of ideas of an outstanding geometer of the first half of the nineteenth century, and of one of the greatest of all geometers.

This translation was based on the first edition of STEINER's work, and only slight modifications of the original were made; for the most part these consisted in the substitution of English for German letters. Slips in the original have naturally been corrected, and a large number of explanatory, historical, and bibliographic notes have been added, but every addition to the original text has been enclosed by asterisks *....*. It is hoped that many readers may be served by the literature references, making possible considerably more extended outlook on matters under discussion.

The title page of the work as published by STEINER was as follows:

Die geometrischen Konstructionen, ausgeführt mittelst der geraden Linie und Eines festen Kreises, als Lehrgegenstand auf höheren Unterrichts-Anstalten und zur praktischen Benutzung; von Jacob Steiner, Doctor der Philosophie, Königlich Preussischem Professor und ordentlichem Lehrer der Mathematik an der Gewerbschule zu Berlin. Mit zwei Kupfertafeln. Berlin, bei Ferdinand Dümmler, 1833. The work contained ii + 110 p. + 2 folding plates. (13 × 21 cm.)

The second German edition bore the title:

Die geometrischen Constructionen, ausgeführt mittelst der geraden Linie und Eines festen Kreises, als Lehrgegenstand auf höhren Unterrichts-Anstalten und zur practischen Benutzung, and appeared in *Jacob Steiner's*

1

Gesammelte Werke, ed. by K. WEIERSTRASS, Berlin, Reimer, v. 1, 1881, p. 461–522, 527, + plates 38–44.   (15.5 × 24.3 cm.)

The next two German editions had the same title and were edited by A. J. v. OETTINGEN in *Ostwald's Klassiker der exakten Wissenschaften* series, no. 60, Leipzig, Engelmann, 1895, 85 p.; second edition [reprint], 1913, 85 p.   (12.2 × 19.8 cm.)   In these editions the figures were first incorporated into the text.

Partial French translation: "Les constructions géométriques exécutées au moyen de lignes droites et d'un cercle fixe, d'après Jacques Steiner (Berlin, 1833)," by ALBERT LÉVY, *Nouvelles Annales de Mathématiques,* v. 67, 1908, p. 390–409.   (13.3 × 21.4 cm.)

Russian translation: *Geometricheskiia Postroeniia vypolniaemyia posredstvom priamoĭ linii i nepodvizhnago kruga, kak predmet prepodavaniia v srednikh uchebnykh zavedeniiakh i dlia prakticheskago primieneniia.* (*1833*) *Perevod stud. P. M. Erokhina i R. I. Hol'tsberga, pod redaktsieĭ Prof. D. M. Sintsova, s prilozheniem biograficheskago ocherka avtora.* (Khar'kovskaia Matematischeskaia Biblioteka no. 1), Khar'kov, Tipografiia i Litografiia M. Zil'berberg i S-v'ia.   Donets-Zakhrzhevskaia ul., sob. d. no. 6, 1910, xvi, 96 p. + 2 folding plates.   (12.5 × 20.5 cm.)   There was a reprint (10,000 copies) of this SINTSOV edition at Moscow, Uchpedagiz, 1939, 80 p. + portrait.   It was one of a series of state publications of books for elementary and secondary schools and teachers.   I have not seen this edition.

Polish translation: *Konstrukcje Gieometryczne Wykonane za pomoca Linji prostej i Stałego Koła.   Przełożył Stefan Kwietniewski.* (Bibljoteka "Wektora." Serja A. No. 4). Warsawa, Gebethner i Wolff, 1915. viii, 71 p. (18 × 25.3 cm.).

It will be observed that in the original title of STEINER'S work a fixed circle is referred to, but no mention is made of its center, which is very necessary in the discussion which follows.   If a parallelogram in the plane of the circle were also given the center of the given circle might be found with a ruler alone.

In one of his lectures at Göttingen, the late Professor DAVID HILBERT raised the question as to whether two or three circles would have to be given in order to determine the center of one of them by means of a ruler only.   This question was discussed by D. CAUER in *Mathematische Annalen,* "Über die Konstruktion des Mittelpunktes eines Kreises mit dem Lineal allein," v. 73, 1913, p. 90–94, and v. 74, 1913, p. 462–

464.   In three cases two circles only are necessary, namely: when the circles intersect, or are tangent, or are concentric.   Otherwise three circles are necessary, and sufficient; in the second article CAUER gives constructions for this case, by F. SCHUR, and by MIERENDORFF.

According to a review in *Jahrbuch über die Fortschritte der Mathematik*, 1910, p. 555, D. D. MORDUCHAĬ-BOLTOVSKOĬ proved that every point which can be constructed with ruler and compasses can be constructed with ruler alone if one is given any arc of a circle (however small) and its center.

II

Was STEINER the first to recognize that any point which can be constructed with ruler and compasses can be constructed with ruler alone, if a circle and its center are given in the plane of construction?   The only earlier writings to be considered in answering this question are those of the French geometer JEAN VICTOR PONCELET (1788–1867). He was an officer in Napoleon's army in 1812, and on the French retreat from Moscow he was captured by the Russians and imprisoned at Saratov, until returned to France in 1814.   During this period he developed the basis for his great work, *Traité des Propriétés Projectives des Figures*, Paris, 1822 (second ed., revised, corrected and enlarged, 2 v., Paris, 1865; there is a reference to STEINER's work, v. 1, p. 414.)   Of the earlier edition, pages 135–136, 187–190 are highly significant. From these it is perfectly clear that the answer to the question formulated above is to be made in the negative, and that PONCELET was not only the first one to conceive this result, but also to point out that every point constructed with ruler and compasses can be constructed with a two-edged ruler alone, such as the carpenter's square.   For literature in connection with this latter result consult "Constructions with a double-edged ruler," *Amer. Math. Mo.*, v. 25, 1918, p. 357–359.   It is interesting to note that while an increase in the number of compasses will not enable us to solve more complicated geometrical problems, two carpenter squares make possible the solution of cubic equations, and in particular the solution of the problems of the Duplication of the Cube, and of the Trisection of an Angle.

III

A few references may be given to the literature of PONCELET-STEINER constructions, as follows:

J. FRISCHAUF, *Die geometrischen Constructionen von L. Mascheroni und J. Steiner.*   Graz, 1869, p. 11–23.

A. ADLER, *Theorie der geometrischen Konstruktionen.*   Leipzig, 1906, p. 83–91.

A. GIACOMINI, "Über die Lösung der geometrischen Aufgaben mit dem Lineal und den linealen Instrumenten: Betrachtungen vom Standpunkte der projectiven Geometrie," in F. ENRIQUES, *Fragen der Elementargeometrie*. V. 2, Leipzig, 1907, p. 78–82, 88–95.

H. P. HUDSON, *Ruler & Compasses*. London, 1916, p. 118–130.

K. YANAGIHARA, "On some methods of construction in elementary geometry," "II. Poncelet-Steiner's constructions," *Tôhoku Mathematical Journal*, v. 16, 1919, p. 45–47.

H. DE VRIES, "Historische Studien II, Over Jacob Steiner's: Die geometrischen Constructionen...," *Nieuw Tijdschrift voor Wiskunde* ,v. 12, 1924, p. 260–288; also in his *Historische Studien*. Groningen, 1926, p. 84–112.

IV

A. ADLER has remarked (Akad. d. Wissen., Vienna, *Sitzungsberichte d. mathematisch-naturw. Kl.*, v. 99, section IIa, 1890, p. 857) that instead of the circle in PONCELET-STEINER constructions might be substituted a given central conic and one of its foci. Then every point constructed with ruler and compasses might be constructed with ruler alone. Also every problem of the third and fourth degree could then be solved with ruler and compasses. This was first proved by H. J. S. SMITH ("Mémoires sur quelques problèmes cubiques et biquadratiques," *Annali di Matematica*, s. 2, v. 3, 1869, p. 112–165, 218–242 = *Collected Mathematical Papers*, v. 2, Oxford, 1894, p. 1–66) and by H. KORTUM (*Ueber geometrische Aufgaben dritten und vierten Grades*. Bonn, 1869, 71 p.). For these memoirs the Prussian Academy of Sciences made a joint award of its STEINER Prize for 1868. Since SMITH pointed out that it was necessary to have only an arc (however small) of the given conic, the result of MORDUCHAÏ-BOLTOVSKOÏ, referred to above, may be regarded as only a particular case of SMITH's result forty years earlier.

SMITH also really anticipated in statement (p. 1–2) the result of F. LONDON, [(a) "Ueber cubische Construction," Deutsche Mathematiker-Vereinigung, *Jahresbericht*, v. 4, 1896, p. 163–165; (b) "Die geometrischen Constructionen dritten und vierten Grades, ausgeführt mittelst der geraden Linie und einer festen Curve dritter Ordnung," *Zeitschrift für Mathem. und Physik*, v. 41, 1896, p. 129–152] who substituted a rational cubic (in particular the cissoid of DIOCLES) for the circle of PONCELET-STEINER constructions, and showed that problems of the third and fourth degree could then be solved with ruler alone. This discussion was developed further in a Münster doctoral dissertation by F. W. M. FERRARI, *Die geometrische Lösung der Aufgaben dritten und vierten Grades mittels des Lineals und einer festen Kurve dritter Ordnung mit Rückkehrpunkt oder reellem Doppelpunkte*. Münster, 1909, 55 p.

JACOB STEINER, c. 1835(?)

From a crayon portrait by NIKLAUS SENN, first published by J. H. GRAF in 1905.

The reader may find it also of interest in this connection to refer to T. VAHLEN, *Konstruktionen und Approximationen*. Leipzig, 1911, p. 76–103.

V

JACOB STEINER was born on March 18, 1796, at the village of Utzensdorf in Canton Bern, Switzerland, where his father was a farmer. He was the youngest of five children (four boys and a girl), who were each called upon, as soon as they were able, to contribute a share of work on the farm.

Young Jacob's opportunities for education were slight, apart from memorizing a catechism and a song book. He first learned to write when he was fourteen years of age. But his mental powers were recognized, and finally when he was eighteen years of age his parents were, with great difficulty, persuaded to allow their son to go to the school of the Swiss educational reformer PESTALOZZI (1746–1827), at Yverdun in Canton Vaud. After a year and a half STEINER was regarded as competent to give instruction in the school in mathematics, and continued this until the autumn of 1818, when he went to Heidelberg in Germany. Here he supported himself by giving private lessons in mathematics until in 1821 he left for Berlin to become a teacher in a gymnasium; but he withdrew to private instruction after a year. He soon became one of the best teachers of mathematics in the city and numbered among his pupils children from prominent families, such as the sons of Prince AUGUST, and WILLIAM VON HUMBOLDT. As a frequent guest at the home of the latter he soon had backing not only for his appointment in 1827 as teacher of mathematics in the Berlin Gewerbschule (industrial school), but also as a royal Prussian professor (Königlich Preussischer Professor) there.

Before this STEINER had become acquainted with the great Norwegian mathematical genius ABEL when he was in Berlin, and also with A. L. CRELLE who in 1826 founded the famous mathematical *Journal für reine und angewandte Mathematik*, which is still in existence. Four of STEINER's papers and one of ABEL's appeared in the first volume of this periodical, where many of STEINER's later papers were also published. This was the beginning of a flood of new discoveries and publications. STEINER's first book was written during the years 1823–26, but was not published till more than a century later. This dealt with the general theory of contact and intersection of circles and of spheres (*Allgemeine Theorie über das Berühren und Schneiden der Kreise und der Kugeln, worunter eine grosse Anzahl neuer Untersuchungen und Sätze vorkommen in einem systematischen Entwicklungsgange dargestellt.*

Edited by R. FUETER and F. GONSETH, Zürich, 1931, xviii, 345 p. + folding plate).

About the time that this volume was written STEINER became intimate with C. G. J. JACOBI, a student at the University of Berlin, but later at the University of Königsberg, where as professor of mathematics, he made notable contributions to research.

STEINER's first volume published during his lifetime was a remarkable work of 1832 (*Systematische Entwicklung der Abhängigkeit geometrischer Gestalten von einander . . .*, part 1. Berlin, 322 p. + 4 plates) in which he laid the foundation of modern synthetic geometry. This was announced as the first of five parts of a great work, but the other parts, as such, were never published. Very soon after this volume appeared, notable honors were conferred on STEINER. Through JACOBI's efforts the University of Königsberg in 1833 conferred on him the honorary degree of Doctor of Philosophy, and in 1834 through the influence of JACOBI and the brothers ALEXANDER and WILLIAM VON HUMBOLDT a new chair of geometry was founded for him at the University of Berlin, and he was at the same time elected a fellow of the Prussian Academy of Sciences. STEINER's third work, the one herewith issued in translation, appeared shortly before his appointment as university professor, when he was 38 years of age. Thus, freed to carry on research uninterruptedly, he continued to hold this position until his death. Because of ill health he spent his last years in Switzerland.

STEINER's lectures on synthetic geometry, published posthumously (*Vorlesungen über synthetische Geometrie*, ed. by C. F. GEISER and H. SCHRÖTER, 1867; third edition by R. STURM, 2 v., Leipzig, 1887, 1898), were those which he delivered in Berlin for a series of years. They seem to contain most of what was planned for the fifth part of the *Systematische Entwicklung*, referred to above.

Many of STEINER's papers were mere announcements of results and in the paper indicated below, R. STURM published a guide to solutions of STEINER problems which various mathematicians had found. The little book by STURM himself, *Maxima und Minima in der elementaren Geometrie*. Leipzig, 1910, iv, 138 p., was developed from important work of STEINER leading finally to the solution of problems which analytically require the calculus of variations.

Perhaps the most important among STEINER's papers are those relating to curves and surfaces, especially the short paper on general properties of algebraic curves ("Allgemeine Eigenschaften algebraischer Curven," *Journal für die reine und angewandte Mathematik*, v. 46, 1854). This contains only results and there is no indication of the method by which they were obtained. Eminent analysts succeeded in proving some of the theorems but L. CREMONA proved all of them, and that by a uniform synthetic method, in his work, *Introduzione ad una Teoria Geometrica delle Curve Piane*. Bologna, 1862.

STEINER's papers were collected, edited by K. WEIERSTRASS, and published by the Prussian Academy of Sciences (*Jacob Steiner's Gesammelte Werke*. Berlin, 2 v., 1881–82). There is a portrait frontispiece in v. 1. The portrait reproduced in the present volume is that first published by J. H. GRAF in 1897. A third very interesting portrait of STEINER as a young man is contained in the 1905 item of GRAF listed below; see also the KOLLROSS publication.

STEINER's mathematical work was confined to geometry treated synthetically, to the total exclusion of analysis which he hated, just as LAGRANGE hated geometry. In this particular field among his contemporaries he was preeminent. His investigations are distinguished by great generality, and fertility of resource.

Real benefit from STEINER's lectures at Berlin was only obtained by the gifted student who worked very hard. The Socratic method which STEINER learned from PESTALOZZI was applied in the University. He frequently interrupted his lectures in order to convince himself that a hearer understood everything. If the answers did not satisfy him, his remarks, especially in the later years, often drove students from his classroom.

After the death of STEINER (at Bern, Switzerland, April 1, 1863) his personal and scientific papers were deposited in the garret of the city library of Bern, where Professor J. H. GRAF discovered them 30 years later. (C. A. EMCH, "Unpublished Steiner manuscripts," *Amer. Math. Mo.*, v. 36, 1929, p. 273–275.) Some volumes of manuscripts are now in the library of the University of Bern.

In accordance with STEINER's will, one-third of his estate amounting to about 90,000 francs was turned over to the Prussian Academy of Sciences to found a STEINER Prize in Geometry. We have already noted that H. J. S. SMITH and H. KORTUM were bracketed for the award in 1868. Other awards have been as follows: R. STURM and L. CREMONA (1866); L. SCHLÄFLI (1870); O. HESSE (1872); L. LINDELÖF (1880); M. NOETHER and G. H. HALPHEN (1882); W. FIEDLER (1884); E. KÖTTER (1886); H. G. ZEUTHEN (1888); no award (1890); S. GUNDELFINGER and F. SCHOTTKY (1895); C. F. GEISER and D. HILBERT and F. LINDEMANN (1900); no award (1905); G. DARBOUX (1910); last award to E. G. TOGLIATTI (1922) for the topic announced for competition in 1910.

A few of many mathematical terms connected with STEINER's name are as follows:

Steiner Ellipse, the minimum ellipse circumscribing a triangle (STEINER, *Gesammelte Werke*, v. 1, p. 199–200; D. M. Y. SOMMERVILLE, *Analytic Conics*, London, 1924, p. 180).

Steiner Points, the fifteen points in which the 60 Pascal lines of a hexagon 123456 inscribed in a conic meet by threes. For example, 123456, 143652, 163254 give one Steiner Point. (J. CASEY, *A Treatise on the Analytic Geometry*..., second ed. Dublin 1893, p. 329.)

Steiner Circle, the circle through any point P of a conic and also the three points where three other circles through P osculate the conic elsewhere. (J. CASEY, *l. c.*, p. 315.) For other use of the term "Steiner Circle" see W. FINDLAYSON, *Mathematical Gazette*, v. 9, 1917, p 88.

Steinerian, the locus of a point whose first polar curve with respect to a given algebraic curve has a double point. (H. HILTON, *Plane Algebraic Curves*. Oxford, 1920, p. 104–106.)

Steiner's Roman Surface, of fourth degree and third class, and such that every tangent plane to it intersects the surface in two conics. So named because it was discovered in 1844 while STEINER was visiting in Rome. It has been a subject of study by many mathematicians (see G. DE LONGCHAMPS, "Étude d'une surface (la surface Romaine de Steiner)," chapter 12 in *Cours de Problèmes de Géométrie Analytique*, v. 3. Paris, 1899, p. 533–576.

More detailed information regarding STEINER's life and work may be found in the following sources:

O. HESSE, "Jacob Steiner," *Journal für die reine und angewandte Mathematik*, v. 62, 1863, p. 199–200.

C. F. GEISER, "Zur Erinnerung an Jakob Steiner. Ein Vortrag gehalten... den 22 August 1873," Schweizer. Natf. Gesell., *Verhandlungen*, v. 56, 1873, p. 215–251. Reprinted, Schaffhausen, 1874, 37 p. Italian translation: *Annali di Matematica*, Milan, s. 2, v. 7, 1876, p. 65–88.

M. CANTOR, in *Allgemeine Deutsche Biographie*, Leipzig, v. 35, 1893, p. 700–703.

Der Briefwechsel zwischen Jakob Steiner und Ludwig Schläfli, herausgegeben von J. H. GRAF; reprinted from *Mitteilungen der Naturforschenden Gesellshaft in Bern*, Bern, 1896, 208 p.

F. BÜTZBERGER, "Zum 100. Geburtstage Jakob Steiners," *Zeitschrift für mathematischen und naturwissenschaftlichen Unterricht*, v. 27, 1896, p. 161–171.

"Bestimmungen für die Steinersche Stiftung," p. 122–124 of *Statuten und Reglements der Königlich Preussischen Akademie der Wissenschaften*, Berlin, 1896.

J. H. GRAF, *Der Mathematiker Jakob Steiner von Utzenstorf. Ein Lebensbild und zugleich eine Würdigung seiner Leistungen. Mit dem Porträt und dem Facsimile eines Briefes Steiners*. Bern, 1897, iv, 54 p. + 2 plates.

J. H. GRAF, *Die Exhumirung Jakob Steiner's und die Einweihung des Grabdenkmals Ludwig Schläfli's anlasslich des hundertsten Geburtstages Steiners am 18*

März 1896, reprinted from *Mitteilungen der Naturforschenden Gesellschaft in Bern*, Bern, 1897, 19 p. + 3 plates.

J. LANGE, *Jacob Steiners Lebensjahre in Berlin 1821–1863. Nach seinen Personalakten dargestellt.* Berlin, 1899, 70 p.

E. LAMPE, "Zur Biographie von Jacob Steiner," *Bibliotheca Mathematica*, s. 3, v. 1, 1900, p. 129–141.

E. KÖTTER, *Die Entwickelung der Synthetischen Geometrie von Monge bis auf Staudt (1847).* Deutsche Mathematiker-Vereinigung, *Jahresbericht*, v. 52, 1901, xxviii, 486 p.

R. STURM, "Zusammenstellung von Arbeiten, welche sich mit Steinerschen Aufgaben beschäftigen," *Bibliotheca Mathematica*, s. 3, v. 4, 1903, p. 160–184.

J. H. GRAF, *Beiträge zur Biographie Jakob Steiners...mit einen bisher unbekannten Porträt Steiners;* reprinted from *Mitteilungen der Naturforschenden Gesellschaft in Bern*, Bern, 1905, 11 p. + 1 plate.

Encyclopædia Britannica, eleventh ed., v. 25, article "Steiner, Jakob," 1911.

F. BÜTZBERGER, *Über bizentrische Polygone, Steinersche Kreis- und Kugelreihen und die Erfindung der Inversion.* Leipzig, 1913, 60 p.

F. CAJORI, *A History of Mathematics*, second ed. New York, 1919, p. 290–292.

L. KOLLROSS, *Jakob Steiner. (Kurze Mathematiker-Biographien, no. 2.) Suppl., Revue de Mathématiques Eléméntaires*, Basel, Dec. 1947, 24 p. There are 3 illustrs. (2 portraits and a facsimile of a page of STEINER ms.).

See also the many references to STEINER and his work in M. CHASLES, *Rapport sur les Progrès de la Géométrie.* Paris, 1870; in W. LOREY, *Das Studium der Mathematik an den deutschen Universitäten seit Anfang des 19. Jahrhunderts.* Leipzig and Berlin, 1916; and in G. LORIA, *Il Passato e il Presente delle Principali Teorie Geometriche. Storia e Bibliografia.* Fourth ed., Padua, 1931.

* * *

Professor STARK desires to record her obligations to Professor GINSBURG for a number of valuable proof suggestions in connection with the translation.

RAYMOND CLARE ARCHIBALD

AUGUST, 1948

INTRODUCTORY SURVEY

§ 1

GEOMETRY in the narrower sense needs for its constructions two instruments, the compasses and ruler. An Italian mathematician, MASCHERONI, has ingeniously shown[1] that all geometrical problems can be solved by means of the compasses alone. On the other hand, some French mathematicians have very recently called attention to the numerous problems whose solution requires simply the use of the ruler,[2] or the drawing of straight lines between given points. Indeed some have already voiced the conjecture that all constructions are possible with ruler alone, provided that some fixed auxiliary circle is given in the plane.[3] The aim of the present little work is to confirm this conjecture. It turns out that this objective may be more easily attained than I at first thought possible and than appeared to be possible, considering the nature of the subject. For, if we closely inspect all constructions arising from unrestricted use of compasses and ruler as we find them in ordinary geometry, we see that, except for the cases where the ruler alone suffices, they depend fundamentally, however complex they may be besides, on the following principal constructions alone:

(a) *to find the intersections of a straight line and a circle*, and

(b) *to find the intersections of two circles.*

For the present more restricted aids it appears that only the first of these two problems is important as a principal problem, that then the solution of all problems depends simply on the following:

(A) *to find the intersections of a straight line and a circle;* the other problem mentioned (b) must and can be reduced to this. When, however, the intersections of a straight line and the given auxiliary circle are given directly, we may next easily solve the following fundamental lemmas, which often arise and which are the basis of most elementary problems:

(c) *to draw parallel lines*[4];

(d) *to multiply at will the length of a given line-segment*[5] *or to divide it into as many equal parts as we choose;*

(e) *to draw lines perpendicular to one another;*

(f) *through a given point to draw a line which makes with a given line an angle equal to an angle given in size and position;*

10

(g) *to bisect a given angle or to multiply it at will;*

(h) *to draw from a given point in any desired direction a line-segment that is equal to a line-segment given in length and position.*]

The method by which these problems are solved is naturally wholly different from that customary in geometry; and indeed to such an extent then are so different that some of these lemmas serve to solve under all circumstances the above-mentioned two chief problems (a), (b); or rather the single principal problem (A). They may be used also to find the intersections of a line and a circle of which only the position and size are given (that is, only the center and radius are given; the circle itself is not drawn), instead of the former being solved by the latter. I cannot decide whether or not I have succeeded in attaining the desired end in the simplest manner; nor am I convinced that in the course I have adopted the best constructions have been always employed. Notwithstanding this, should the subject inspire some interest, with the eager pursuit of geometry in our time deficiencies would soon be supplied by others, and I might then indeed count upon some indulgence.

If the constructions of MASCHERONI are of great benefit to instrument makers, especially in the construction of astronomical instruments, as he declares,[6] then, on the other hand, the present publication might be not less serviceable to engineers and surveyors. Concerning this, however, I shall await the skilled judgment of these experts.

§ 2

The theorems and properties of figures on which the solution of the above-mentioned problems (§ 1) depends are contained among others partly in the first part of *Systematische Entwickelung der Abhängigkeit geometrischer Gestalten von einander*, and partly in the memoir, "Einige geometrische Betrachtungen" (*Journal für Mathematik*, vol. 1, p. 161)[7]; so that with reference to these publications the proposed problems could be dispatched in the space of a few pages. Since, however, the present little book may easily come into the hands of many people who do not possess these writings, I regard it as expedient to repeat those theorems and properties briefly here; wherefore I have taken pains to present them in as elementary a manner as possible. Accordingly, the present work consists of three chapters, whose contents are as follows:

First Chapter. Some properties of rectilinear figures, with regard to transversals, harmonic rays, and points; constructions with ruler alone under definite hypotheses, i. e., when either parallel lines or line-segments divided in known ratio are given, other line-segments given in magnitude and position may be multipled and divided at will, and other parallel lines may be drawn (also right angles may be bisected and given angles multiplied as we choose).

· *Second Chapter.*   Concerning the circle.   I.   Harmonic properties of the circle.   II.   Centers of similitude (or points of projection) of two or more circles.   III.   Power with respect to circles;   (A) the locus of points with equal powers;   (B) common power, with respect to centers of similitude.

Third Chapter.   Solution of all geometrical problems by means of the ruler alone, when any fixed auxiliary circle is given[8]; containing the above-mentioned eight problems (§ 1, a to h).   Concluding Comment.

Furthermore, there are set forth in an appendix a few other fundamental problems about conics, which are to serve as appropriate examples of the application of the present methods.

Chapter I

SOME PROPERTIES OF RECTILINEAR FIGURES, AND RE-SULTING CONSTRUCTIONS WITH RULER ALONE

1. HARMONIC RAYS AND POINTS, TRANSVERSALS

§3

I.   Let ABC (Fig. 1) be any triangle; from the vertex B draw the ray b to the midpoint B' of the base AC and the ray d parallel to AC. If we draw through the midpoint B' any straight line, or transversal, $A'D'$,

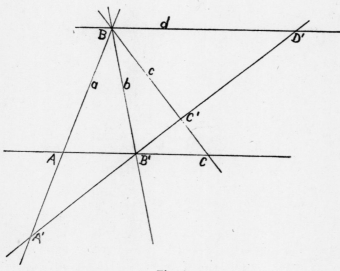

Fig. 1

this transversal will be cut by the two sides a and c and by the rays b and d in the four points A', B', C', and D' so that

$$AB':BD' = A'B':A'D' \text{ (because } \Delta A'AB' \sim \Delta A'BD'),$$

and

$$CB':BD' = C'B':C'D' \text{ (because } \Delta C'CB' \sim \Delta C'BD').$$

13

Therefore, because $AB' = CB'$,

$$A'B':A'D' = C'B':C'D',$$

or

$$A'B':B'C' = A'D':C'D';$$

that is, the line-segment $A'D'$ is divided into three parts such that the ratio of the first, $A'B'$, to the second, $B'C'$, equals the ratio of the whole, $A'D'$, to the third, $C'D'$.

By virtue of this property the four points A', B', C', and D' are called "*four harmonic points*," and A' and C', as well as B' and D', are called "*harmonically conjugate points*." So, also, the four rays a, b, c, and d are called *four harmonic rays*,[9] and a and c as well as b and d are said to be "*harmonically conjugate rays*."

II.   If the rays a, b, c, and d are assumed fixed and of unlimited length, not only do they divide harmonically every transversal passing through B', but evidently any transversal whatever is cut by them in four harmonic points; for, in whatever point such a transversal meets the ray b, we may always suppose a line drawn through the point parallel to AC, and then the preceding proof is applicable. In particular, if the transversal is parallel to one of the four harmonic rays a, b, c, and d, as for example AC to d, then the point B' in which it cuts the ray b, the harmonic conjugate of the parallel ray d, is the midpoint of the portion of the line between A' and C', the points in which it is cut by the other two rays a and c. Conversely, if the conclusion of the last statement holds, the transversal is parallel to the ray d.

On the other hand, if the four harmonic points A', B', C', and D' are taken as fixed, it follows in a similar manner that every four rays a, b, c, and d, which are drawn from any arbitary point B through the harmonic points, are four harmonic rays.

III.   It is easy to see that if we are given three concurrent rays two of which are to be harmonically conjugate, then it is possible to have only a singly-determinate ray which is the harmonic conjugate of the third ray. If, for example, the three rays a, c, and d are given and if, say, a and c are harmonically conjugate, suppose any line AC drawn parallel to the third ray d. Then the fourth ray b, the harmonic conjugate of d, must pass through B', the midpoint of AC, and is therefore definitely determined. Or, if through any point of the third ray, as the point B' of the ray b, (the three rays a, b, and c being given and a and c being harmonically conjugate) we suppose a line-segment AC drawn between a and c so that it is bisected at B', then the ray d parallel to AC will be the only possible fourth harmonic ray, conjugate to b. Similar results apply to four harmonic points A', B', C', and D'.

IV.   In particular, if the triangle ABC is isosceles, $BA = BC$, then the ray b, since it passes through the midpoint B' of the base AC, will be perpendicular to it as well as to the ray d, and will make equal angles with the rays a and c.   Hence angle $(ab) = (bc)$, and therefore d must also form equal angles with these rays, or $(ad) = (dc)$.   That is to say:

If of four harmonic rays a, b, c, and d one, such as b, makes equal angles with two harmonically conjugate rays, a and c, then the same is true of its harmonic conjugate d, and the rays b and d are perpendicular to each other. Conversely, if of four harmonic rays two that are harmonically conjugate, b and d, are perpendicular, they bisect the angles formed by the other two rays, a and c.

§ 4

Any four lines a, c, a_1, and c_1 (Fig. 2) in a plane, which in general cut one another by pairs in six points A, C, F, G, H, and I, form what is called a *"complete quadrilateral."*[10]   Such a quadrilateral has, as we ob-

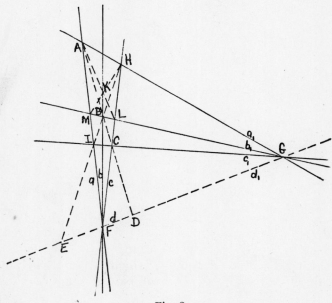

Fig. 2

serve, three diagonals AC, GF, and HI, which cut one another in the three points B, D, and E.   It is easy to show that these three diagonals divide one another harmonically,[11] namely as follows.

To the three rays a, c, and d suppose a fourth ray b, the harmonic conjugate of d, is added; and in the same way to the three rays a_1, c_1, and d_1[12] a fourth ray b_1, the harmonic conjugate of d_1; then each of the two rays b and b_1 must cut the diagonal ACD in the point B, which is the fourth harmonic point to the three given points A, C, and D and conjugate to D (§ 3). In the same way both rays b and b_1 cut the diagonal HIE in the point B, which is the fourth harmonic point to the three points H, I, and E and conjugate to E. Since, however, b and b_1 can have only one point B in common, this point must at the same time be the intersection of the diagonals AC and HI, from which we see that these diagonals are divided harmonically. In a similar way it can be shown that the third diagonal GF is divided harmonically by the other two at the points D and E. Consequently:

In every complete quadrilateral each of the three diagonals is divided harmonically by the other two; i. e., the points in which one of the three diagonals is cut by the other two are harmonically conjugate to the vertices which it connects,[13] for example A, B, C, and D are harmonic and B and D are harmonically conjugate points.

§ 5

Among the numerous deductions and applications which may be made of the last proposition (§ 4), only a few, and indeed those immediately following, are selected.

I. *By means of the ruler alone find the fourth harmonic point to any three given collinear points.*

(a) If the three given points are G, D, and F (Fig. 2) and if the fourth harmonic point E, conjugate to D, is to be found, draw through any point A the lines AG, AD, and AF. Then take any point C on AD and draw the lines GCI and FCH, determining the two intersections I and H. Finally, draw the line HI, and this will give the desired point E. Or:

(b) If G, F, and E are given and the fourth harmonic point D, conjugate to E, is to be found, draw to any point A the lines FA and GA; cut them by any line EIH, passing through E, in the points I and H. Draw forthwith the lines GI and FH which intersect each other in C, and draw, finally, the line AC; this will pass through the desired point D.[14]

II. *By means of the ruler alone find the fourth harmonic ray to any three concurrent rays.*

If the three rays a, c, and d (Fig. 2) are given and the fourth harmonic ray b, conjugate to d, is to be found, draw through any point G of the ray d any two lines GA and GI, which cut the rays a and c in A, I, C, and H. Then draw the lines AC and HI, which intersect each other in B, and FB will be the desired ray.

In the same way, if the rays a, b, and c are given, we find the fourth ray d, the harmonic conjugate of b.

III.   *If a right angle and any other angle have the same vertex and a common side, then double the second angle by means of the ruler alone.*

Taking (bd) (Fig. 1) as the right angle and (bc) as the other angle, to the three rays b, c, and d seek a fourth harmonic ray a (II), conjugate to c. Then by virtue of (§3, IV) $(ab) = (bc)$, and therefore (ac) is the desired doubled angle.

IV.   *If of three concurrent rays one forms equal angles with the other two, find by means of the ruler alone a fourth ray which also makes equal angles with the last two, and is perpendicular to the first.*

As in the preceding problem, the solution of this one depends upon (II) and (§ 3, IV).

V.   *If any two lines a and c (Fig. 2) are cut by any concurrent lines a_1, b_1, c_1, ..., passing through a point G, and we join the intersections of a and c with every two of the latter crosswise by a pair of lines, as AC and HI, AL and HM; then all points, as B and K, in which these line-pairs intersect, lie on a definite line b, which goes through the intersection F of the two first-named lines a and c,[15] and which is: (1) the fourth harmonic line of a, c, and FG or d; and (2) the harmonic conjugate of d.*

The correctness of this proposition is shown, as one readily sees, by (II) or (§ 4).

VI.   *Through a given point construct by means of the ruler alone a line which is directed to one and the same point as each of two given lines, if this point is inaccessible because of obstacles.*

Let B, say (Fig. 2), be the given point, and AM and HL the given lines which cannot, however, be extended to the point F towards which they are directed. Draw the lines AB and HB, which cut the given lines in C and I. Draw also the lines AH and IC, which intersect in G. Through this point G draw any line GM, not necessarily passing through B, which cuts the given lines in M and L. Then straightway draw AL and HM, which intersect each other in K; and the line KB will be a solution of the problem. The method remains the same, whatever the position of the point B with respect to the given lines AM and HL, as for example the position of G. In the same way these lines can have any position whatever with respect to each other, for example be parallel.

It is readily seen that the correctness of this solution rests on the preceding proposition (V). (Compare *Abhängigkeit geometrischer Gestalten*, part I, page 77.)

2. Constructions by Means of the Ruler Alone, Under Certain Hypotheses

A. When Parallels, or rationally divided Segments, are given.

§ 6

In consideration of the above-mentioned problem (§ 5, I) an especially important case, which must be examined more particularly, presents itself.

If we have the special case, that of the three given points *G*, *F*, and *D*, the point *D* lies midway between *G* and *F*, then the fourth harmonic point *E*, conjugate to *D*, moves off to infinity; i. e., the line *HI* by which it is found must be parallel to the given line *GDF*. And conversely, if two sides *AG* and *AF* of any triangle *GAF* are cut by any line *HI* (Fig. 3) parallel to the base *GF*, the intersections *H* and *I* joined with the opposite vertices on the base by line-segments *FH* and *GI*, intersecting each other in *C*, and if we draw through this point and through the vertex *A* of the triangle the line *ACD;* then this always goes through the midpoint *D* of the base.

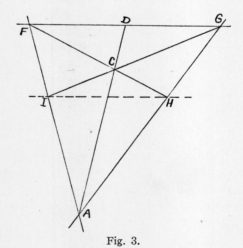

Fig. 3.

The solutions of the following problems are based upon this result.

I. *If on a line we are given three points G, D, and F (Fig. 3), one of which, as D, lies midway between the othert wo, then by means of the ruler alone through any point whatever, as H, a parallel to that line is to be drawn.*

Draw the lines GH and $FH;$ take any point A on GH, and draw AD and AF. Through the intersection C of FH and AD draw from G the line GCI which cuts AF in I. Then, finally, HI is the desired parallel.

II. *Given any two parallel lines GF and HI (Fig. 3), to bisect any given segment on one or the other, as the segment GF.*

Draw from any point A to the end-points G and F of the given segment the lines AG and AF which cut the other parallel in H and I. In case the point A lies between the parallels, as at C, or on the further side of GF, we must produce the line-segments AG and AF until they cut HI. Connect these intersections with the end-points by line-segments HF and IG, which intersect each other in some point C. Finally, through this and through the given point A draw the line ACD. Then this will pass through the middle point D of the given segment GF.

III. *If any two parallel lines are given, through any given point a third parallel is to be drawn.*[16]

By means of (II) bisect any segment of one of the two given lines, and the problem is reduced to (I).

IV. *If we are given two parallel lines and a finite segment on one of them, we are*

(a) *to mark off on the same line, from any given point, another segment whose length is any multiple, say the nth multiple, of the given segment;* or

(b) *to divide the given segment into any given number of equal parts, or into two parts which have the ratio of two given integers;* or finally,

(c) *to find another segment in the same line, which has a given rational ratio to the given segment.*

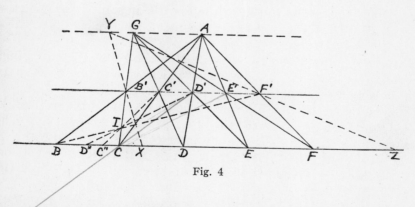

Fig. 4

Let BF and $B'F'$ (Fig. 4) be the given parallels and BC the given segment. Draw through any point A a third parallel AG (III), and draw to the end-points of the segment the lines AB and AC, which cut the second parallel in B' and C'. As soon as we draw the line CB', which meets the third parallel in G, and draw $GC'D$, it is easy to see that $DC = BC$, and consequently BD is twice as long as the given segment BC. If we now continue by drawing the line AD and then $GD'E$; next, also, the line AE and afterwards $GE'F$, etc.; the segments BC CD, DE, EF, ... will evidently be equal in size, so that we can in this manner obtain any multiple of the segment BC, as, for example, BF its quadruple.

(a) Now if such a multiple is to be cut off from any given point X, draw the line XB', or XF', produce it if necessary until it cuts AG in Y, and draw $YF'Z$. Then XZ is the desired n-tuplye, here fourth multiple, of the segment BC.

(b) To divide the given segment BC into n equal parts, draw, if $B'F'$ is the nth multiple of $B'C'$, the lines CB' and BF', which intersect each other in I, and forthwith draw $C'IC''$, $D'ID''$, $E'IE''$, ... Then the segments CC'', $C''D''$, $D''E''$, ... are equal to one another, and indeed each is the nth part of the given segment BC.

To divide the given segment BC into two parts which have the ratio of two given integers p and q, $B'F'$ must be the $(p + q)$th multiple of $B'C'$. Then count off from B' p segments $B'C'$, $C'D'$, ... Draw from the end-point of the last one, as for example from D', the line $D'ID''$. Then the parts cut off, CD'' and BD'', will have the ratio $p:q$.

(c) Finally, to find a segment whose ratio to the given segment is as $q:p$, draw, if $F'D'$ and $D'B'$ are also in the ratio of $q:p$, the lines BB' and CD'; and from the point in which these intersect draw a line through F'. Then this will meet the line BC in some point which we may call W. CW is then the desired segment, $i.\ e.$, we have $BC:CW = p:q$.

NOTE: If from the given segment BC merely one definite simple part is to be cut off, i. e., a piece which is to the whole as $1:n$ where n is an integer, then we may proceed as follows:

From any point A (Fig. 5) draw to the end-points of the segment the lines AB and AC, which meet the other parallel in B' and C'. Then draw the lines BC' and CB', which intersect in D', and also the line $AD'D$. Then CD is half the given length BC. If, furthermore, we now draw the line $C'D$, meeting CB' in E', and forthwith draw $AE'E$, then $CE = \frac{1}{3} BC$. For, because of the complete quadrilateral $AC'E'D'$ whose three diagonals are AE', $C'D'$, and CD, the four points B, D, E, and C are harmonic (§ 4), so that we have

$$CE:ED = CB:DB,[17]$$

from which it follows, since

$$DB = CD = \tfrac{1}{2}CB,$$

that

$$CE = \tfrac{1}{3}CB.$$

In a similar manner it follows that if we draw further the line $C'E$, which cuts CB' in F', and then draw $AF'F$, that in that case $CF = \tfrac{1}{4}CB$; and that by the same process we obtain $CG = \tfrac{1}{5}CB$, and so on.

This ingenious method seems to have been first employed by a French artillery captain, BRIANCHON (*Application de la Théorie des Transversales*. Paris, 1818, p. 37). He takes up also several of the preceding problems and shows especially what advantageous applications could be made of such problems in the field, in war, etc. On this account I refer military men and surveyors to his work.

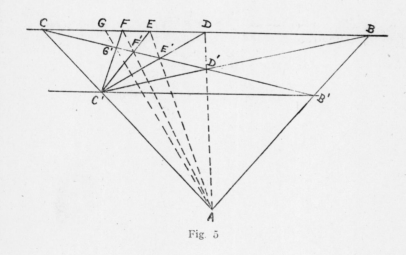

Fig. 5

§ 7[17a]

By means of a ruler alone draw through any point a parallel to a line in which are two adjacent segments BD and DC (Fig. 6) having a given ratio to each other.

Since this problem may well have more theoretical interest than practical use, I shall only briefly indicate here the possibility of its solution, and leave to others the discovery of the easiest and most convenient method.

The problem may be regarded solved as soon as we have found on the given line any three points, one of which is equally distant from the other two (§ 6, I).

The given rational relation of the given segments BD and DC may always, in whatever form it is given, be expressed by two integers a and b which are prime to each other. Let it be supposed that $a > b$. To the three given points B, D, and C, construct the fourth harmonic point E (§ 5, I), conjugate to D. Then we have:

$$BD:CD = BE:CE;$$

or, if we substitute for the lines the numbers corresponding to them and let $x = CE$,

$$a:b = (a + b + x):x$$

and consequently,

$$x = \frac{b(a + b)}{a - b}.$$

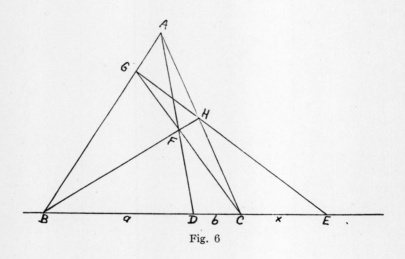

Fig. 6

If we set $BC = a + b = y$, we have

$$x:y = \frac{b(a + b)}{a - b}:(a + b)$$

or

$$x:y = b:(a - b);\qquad(1)$$

that is to say:

From the given segments BD and CD, which are in the ratio of the numbers a and b, may be found two new segments BC and CE or y and x which are in the ratio of the difference of the given numbers, a — b, and the smaller number, b. Therefore, by repeated use of this method we shall finally obtain two segments which are equal, i. e., we shall have three points one of which lies midway between the other two; and the proposed problem is thereby reduced to the one discussed above (§ 6, I). For if, for example, the difference $a - b$ is greater than b, by a new construction we get two segments which have the ratio $b:(a - 2b)$. Thus we may continue until we get two segments which have the ratio $b:(a - nb)$, where the remainder $a - nb$ is less than b and is equal to some number c. Then we find further two segments which have the ratio $c:(b - c)$, and so on. Since a, b, c, . . . are integers each smaller than the preceding, this must necessarily lead at last, to two segments which have the ratio $1:1$.

If DE, or $b + x$, is set equal to z, we have on substituting for x the above value

$$a:z = a:\left[b + \frac{b(a + b)}{a - b}\right],$$

or

$$a:z = (a - b):2b;\qquad(2)$$

i. e., by the same constructions we get two segments BD and DE which are to each other as the difference of the given numbers, $a - b$, is to twice the smaller number, $2b$; by which process we may in certain cases approach the desired ratio $1:1$ more quickly.

If, for example,

$$(\alpha)\quad a = 2 \text{ and } b = 1,$$

then $x = 3$, and therefore C is midway between B and E; and if

$$(\beta)\quad a = 3 \text{ and } b = 1,$$

then $x = 2$, and consequently D is midway between B and E. Each of these two cases demands then only a single auxiliary construction.

B. *When two Pairs of Parallels, or two rationally divided Segments, or Parallels and rationally divided Segments at the same time, are given.*

§ 8

I.   *If in a plane we are given any two pairs of parallel lines, or any parallelogram, then (by means of a ruler alone) we are*

(a) *to draw parallel lines in all directions, i. e., to draw through any given point a parallel to any given line,*[18] *and*

(b) *to increase or divide a given segment in any given ratio.*[19]

Let AB and DC, AD and BC (Fig. 7) be the given parallels and therefore $ABCD$ the given parallelogram, whose diagonals AC and BD intersect in E. Through the point E draw to one of the two pairs of parallels, as to AD and BC, a third parallel EF which, of course, lies midway between AD and BC; i. e., it is equally distant from them, so that these three parallels cut every other line (not parallel to them) in three such points that one of them lies midway between the other two.

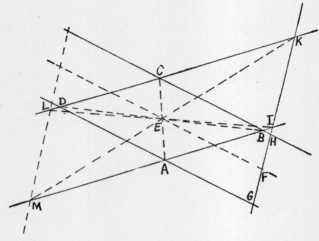

Fig. 7

Now if a line as GK is given, it is cut by the three parallels in three points, G, F, and H, one of which, F, is midway between the other two, G and H. Then the requirement (a): "through any point to draw a parallel to the line GK" can be satisfied, by virtue of (§6, I).

Or, instead of drawing the third parallel EF, we may proceed as follows. Through the points I and K in which the given line GK cuts the parallels AB and DC draw the lines IE and KE, which meet these parallels in L and M. The line LM will evidently be parallel to IK and then through any point, according to (§ 6, III), a parallel to IK may be drawn.

The second requirement (b) may be dispatched by the help of the first and by the method (§ 6, IV).[20]

II.   *If in a plane we are given either*

(a) *three parallels, which cut any fourth line in a given rational ratio;* or

(b) *any two segments in two parallels, which have a given rational ratio;* or

(c) *any two parallels and any segment divided in a given rational ratio; or finally*

(d) *any two non-parallel segments, both of which are divided in given rational ratios, it is required*

(α) *to draw parallels in any direction,* and

(β) *to increase or divide any given segment in any given rational ratio.*

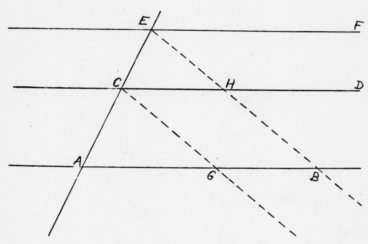

Fig. 8

Case a.   If the three parallels AB, CD, and EF (Fig. 8) cut a fourth line AE so that its segments AC and CE have the ratio $p:q$, where p and q are integers prime to each other, multiply in one parallel, as in AB, an arbitrary segment and take AG equal to the pth multiple and GB equal to the qth multiple of this segment (§ 6, IV, a).   Then draw the lines GC and BE; these will be parallel, because $AC:CE = AG:GB = p:q$. The proposed problem is thus reduced to the preceding (I).

To get a second pair of parallels we might also, in consequence of § 7, draw any parallel to the segment AE which is divided in a known rational ratio; but that method would be longer than the first.

Case b. Let *AB* and *CD* (Fig. 8) be the given parallels and *AB* and *CH* the given segments, which have to each other the ratio of two given integers *p* and *q*. Draw through the end-points of the segments the lines *AC* and *BH*, which intersect in some point *E*. (We could as well draw the lines *AH* and *BC*.) Then we shall have, because of the similar triangles *AEB* and *CEH*, for example,

$$AE:CE = AB:CH = p:q.$$

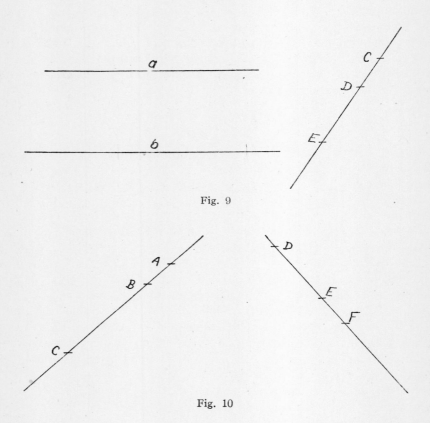

Fig. 9

Fig. 10

Therefore, also, the ratio of the segments *AC*:*CE* is given, for it equals $(p - q):q$; hence the present case is reduced to the preceding (a). It is easy to see that in doing this it is not necessary to draw the third parallel *EF*.

Case c. Let *a* and *b* (Fig. 9) be the given parallels and *CE* the given segment, divided at *D* so that the segments *CD* and *DE* are in the ratio of the two integers p and q. Draw through the points C, D, and E three lines parallel to the lines a and b (§ 6, III). Then we have the first case (a).

Or, draw through any point a parallel to CE (§ 7); then we have reduced the problem to one mentioned above (I).

Case d. If AC and DF (Fig. 10) are the given segments, which are divided at the points B and E in given ratios so that $AB:BC = p:q$ and $DE:EF = r:s$, where p, q, r, and s are given integers, draw through any point a parallel to AC and through the same or any other point a parallel to DF (§ 7). Then we have reduced the problem to a preceding one (I). Or, draw through two points of one line, as through F and E, parallels to the other line AC (§ 7). Then we have reduced the problem to case (a), and the construction will in most cases be somewhat shorter on the whole than the preceding.

C. *If a Square is given*

§ 9

Besides the problems which have been previously solved by the help of an arbitrary parallelogram (§ 8, I), in the special case where the parallelogram is a square the following additional problems, among others, may be solved.

If in a plane any square is given,

(a) *drop a perpendicular on any given line from any given point;*

(b) *bisect any given right angle;*

(c) *multiply a given angle by any number.*

Let $ABCD$ (Fig. 11) be the given square and E the point of intersection of its diagonals AC and BD, and therefore its center.

Draw through the center any line GF. Then it is easy to find that line IK which is perpendicular to it at the center E. For, draw from F the line FH parallel to the side BC or AD (§ 6, III), and then from the point H in which this meets the side AB draw the line HI parallel to the diagonal AEC (§ 6, I). Then the line IEK is perpendicular to FEG. By virtue of this construction it is easy to see that $FC = HB = BI$; and further that $BE = CE$, and that angle EBI = angle ECF. Therefore the triangles EBI and ECF are congruent. Hence, angle BEI = angle CEF, and therefore angle BEC = angle IEF = a right angle.

Since from the congruence of the triangles BEI and CEF it follows, also, that $EI = EF$, the triangle IEF is consequently isosceles, so that the line EL which bisects the vertical angle E is perpendicular to the base IF. Therefore this angle is easily bisected. For, to this end draw EN parallel to IF and GK; and draw in the manner just indicated MEL perpendicular to EN. Then EL will bisect the right angle IEF.

If it is now desired to drop a perpendicular on any given line G_1F_1 from any given point I_1 (a), then draw through the midpoint E the line FG parallel to F_1G_1, erect KEI perpendicular to FEG, and draw through the given point I_1 the line I_1E_1 parallel to IEK (§ 6, I). Then evidently the construction desired has been accomplished. It is clear that the procedure remains the same if a line is to be drawn perpendicular to the given line F_1G_1 at a point E_1 on it.

If we now wish to bisect any given right angle $F_1E_1I_1$ (b), draw EF parallel to E_1F_1 and EI parallel to E_1I_1, bisect the angle FEI by means of the line EL, and, finally, draw through the point E_1 the line E_1L_1 parallel to EL. This evidently solves the problem.

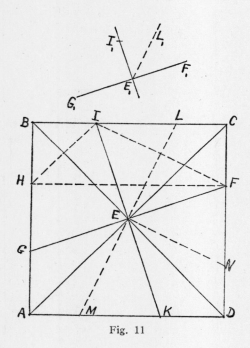

Fig. 11

Finally, case (c) is easily dispatched by means of case (a) and an earlier problem (§ 5, III). For if at the vertex of the given angle whose sides may be called a and b we erect a perpendicular to one of its sides, b, as has just been explained (a), then the given angle can be immediately doubled, by the method of § 5, III. We have then two angles (ab) and (bc) which are equal to each other and have a common side b, so that the angle (ac) is twice the given angle (ab). If we now further erect a perpendicular to the side c in the same way and double the two angles (cb) and (ca), having this side in common, then we have two new sides d and e; and (ad) is three times the given angle (ab), and (ae) is four times (ab).   In the same way we now get by means of a perpendicular to the last side e angles that are five, six, seven, and eight times the given angle, and then by a new perpendicular nine to sixteen times the given angle; and so on.   By the nth perpendicular we obtain angles that are $(2^n + 1)$ to 2^{n+1} times the given angle.

Chapter II

SOME PROPERTIES OF THE CIRCLE

1. HARMONIC PROPERTIES[21]

§ 10

I. If A, B, C, and D (Fig. 12) are any four harmonic points, every four rays a, b, c, d which pass through them from any point B' are also harmonic (§ 3). If the four points are taken as fixed and if two of the rays which are harmonically conjugate, as a and c, are at right angles and consequently bisect the angles formed by the other two rays, so that $(ab) = (ad)$[22] and $(cb) = (cd)$ (§ 3, IV), then, of course, the locus of the point B' is a circle (M), which has the segment AC as diameter.

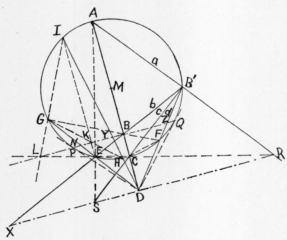

Fig. 12

The rays b and d meet the circle (M) a second time in E and F. Since $(bc) = (dc)$, arc EC = arc FC. Therefore it follows, if we draw the equal chords EC and FC, that angle EBC = angle FBC and angle EDC = angle FDC. Furthermore, it follows from this that BQ, the fourth harmonic ray to the three rays BE, BC, and BF and the conjugate to BC, is perpendicular to BC and makes equal angles with the

30

other two rays BE, or BB', and BF; i. e., angle $B'BQ =$ angle FBQ. So, also, DX, the fourth harmonic ray to the three rays DE, DC, and DF and the conjugate to DC, is perpendicular to DC and makes equal angles with the other two rays, DE and DF. Because these two sets of rays are harmonic it also follows, finally, that D, F, Z [where BQ meets d], and B', as well as B', B, E, and X, form a harmonic range.

Since in this discussion the four points A, B, C, and D, as well as the circle (M), are supposed fixed, so the lines BQ and DX, the first of which intersects the circle in P and Q are also fixed. On the other hand, the rays b, d, BF, and DE change their position together with the point B', for they turn about the fixed points B and D, while B' moves along the circle. Since, furthermore, the variable angles $B'BQ$ and QBF are always equal, B' and F must approach the fixed point Q at the same time, so that they finally coincide with it simultaneously. Consequently the line DQ, with which the ray d merges in this case, is tangent to the circle. (The last result follows, also, from the fact that if we imagine the point B' arriving at the fixed point Q and then think of the rays QA, QB, QC, and QD as drawn, these rays are harmonic, and moreover QA and QC are perpendicular to each other. Therefore angle $CQB =$ angle $CQD =$ angle CPB; and therefore DQ is a tangent.[23]) It follows in the same way that DP is tangent to the circle.

From these considerations the following proposition, among others, results:

If we draw through any fixed point, B or D, any line, such as $B'BEX$ or $DFZB'$, which cuts a fixed circle (M), the locus of the point X or Z (which is the fourth harmonic point to the points of intersection, B' and E or F and B', and the fixed point, B or D, and is the conjugate to the last point mentioned), is a fixed line, XD or ZB, perpendicular to the line $ABCD$, the diameter of the circle which passes through the fixed point. XD lies outside the circle or ZB cuts it, according as the fixed point is B, inside, or D, outside the circle. In the latter case, where the fixed point D lies outside the circle, the above-mentioned corresponding line-locus ZB cuts the circle in those points P and Q at which it is in contact with the tangents, DP and DQ, drawn from the fixed point D.

On account of this reciprocal relation between the point, B or D, which is always fixed, and the corresponding line-locus, XD or ZB, the former is called the "*pole*"[24] of the latter, and the latter is called the "*polar*"[25] of the point, with respect to the fixed circle.

II.   If we draw from the fixed point D any two secants of the circle (M), as DG and DI, the four points of intersection E, G, H, and I determine four lines HEL, IGL, EKI, and GKH, or a complete quadrilateral, whose diagonals cut one another harmonically[26] (§ 4). Then the two diagonals EG and HI[27] are cut by the third KL in those points N and Y which are, respectively, the fourth harmonic points to the three points D, E, G, and D, H, I, and conjugate to D. Since, however, on account of the preceding proposition (I), these very lines DEG and DHI are cut by the line PBQ in the same harmonic points N and Y, the diagonal KL must coincide with the line PQ; i. e., the points K and L must lie on PQ, the polar of the point D. In the same way it follows that if we draw through the point B any two secants $B'BE$ and ABC (of which the latter need not be a diameter), their four points of intersection with the circle, B', E, A, and C, determine a complete quadrilateral AES, $B'CS$, $AB'R$, ECR, whose third diagonal RS must cut the other two $B'E$ and AC in those points X and D, which are the fourth harmonic points to B', B, E, and A, B, C, respectively, and conjugate to B. Therefore, the diagonal RS coincides with XD, the polar of the point B. Hence:

If we draw from any fixed point, D or B, any two secants, DG and DI, or $B'E$ and AC, to a fixed circle (M), then their four points of intersection, E, G, H, I or B', E, A, C, determine a (simple) quadrangle (which has those secants as diagonals, and) whose pairs of opposite sides, HE and IG EI and GH, or $B'C$ and AE, AB' and EC, intersect in the points L and K or S and R on the polar PQ or XD, of the given fixed point, D or B.[28]

III. On account of this proposition (II) the polar of the point L must therefore pass through the points D and K, since HE and IG are the two secants passing through this point. But in consequence of (I) it goes, also, through the points of contact of the tangents drawn from the point L to the circle. Hence we may conclude that the polar of every arbitrary point L which lies on the line PQ, but on the outside of the circle, that is, on one or the other side in which PQ produced lies, passes through the pole D of this line; and that, conversely, the pole of every secant passing through the fixed point D lies on PQ (the polar of this point) but outside the circle; so that the tangents drawn to the circle at the points of intersection of the secant, as at H and I, in the case of the secant DHI, intersect on the above-mentioned polar. But the polars of all points which lie within the circle on the line PQ, that is, on the line-segment PQ, pass, also, through the pole D of this line. For if we imagine, for example, the polar of the point Y, this must meet the line IYH in that point which is the fourth harmonic point to the three points I, Y, H, and is the conjugate to Y (I). Therefore, it must meet the line in the point D.

In the same way it follows that the polar of every point on the fixed line XD (which does not cut the circle) passes through B, the pole of XD. For, if we consider the polar of the point X, it must meet the line

XEB' in that point which is the fourth harmonic point to the three points *X*, *E*, *B'*, and is the conjugate to *X* (I). Since, however, on account of the reasoning above the point *B* possesses this property, the line must accordingly pass through *B*. As the point *X* lies outside the circle, we may draw tangents from it to the circle; and its polar passes through their points of contact (I).

From these considerations the following propositions result:

1.   *If a point lies on any line (as L or Y on PQ, or X or R on XD), its polar passes through the line's pole (D or B).*

Or in other words, more in detail:

2.   *The polars of all points lying on any line (PQ or XD) cut one another in a fixed point (D or B); namely, in the pole of that line.*[29] And conversely: *The poles of all lines passing through a fixed point (D or B) lie on the polar (PQ or XD) of that fixed point.*

3.   *If we imagine two tangents to a fixed circle (M) so to move that their point of intersection with each other, L or X, traces out any fixed line, PQ or XR, the line passing through their points of tangency turns about some definite fixed point, D or B.* And conversely: *If a secant of a fixed circle turns about any fixed point, D or B, the point of intersection of the tangents through whose points of contact the secant passes moves along some definite line PQ or XR.*

IV.   The preceding considerations afford convenient means for solving the following problems by means of the ruler alone.

1.   *If in a plane any circle (M) is given, find (a) the polar of any given point,* and (b) *the pole of any given line.*

Let *D* or *B* (Fig. 12) be the given point. Draw through it any two secants, as *DG* and *DI*, or *B'E* and *AC*. Connect the four points of intersection, *E*, *G*, *H*, and *I*, or *B'*, *E*, *A*, and *C*, in which they cut the circle (*M*) in couples by two pairs of lines *HE*, *IG* and *HG*, *IE*, or *B'C*, *AE* and *AB'*, *EC*. Their points of intersection, *L* and *K*, or *S* and *R*, will then lie on the desired line (a), which is thus immediately found.

Again, if the line *PQ*, or *XR*, is given (b), in the manner just indicated seek the polars of any two points of the same, as of *L* and *Y*, or *X* and *S*. Then their point of intersection will be the desired pole (III).

2.   *From a given point D outside a given circle (M) draw the tangents to the circle.*[30]

Construct the polar *PQ* of the given point *D* (1, a) and connect the points *P* and *Q* in which it cuts the circle with the given point by lines *DP* and *DQ*. Then these are the desired tangents.

NOTE: Other propositions, which follow immediately from the above speculation and which relate, in part, to triangles, quadrangles, etc., inscribed in and circumscribed about a circle, are here passed over as lying too far away from the present purpose. These may be found, together with the preceding propositions and exercises, in the above-mentioned work (*Systematische Entwickelung*, etc.) demonstrated in a manner that is comprehensive and adapted to the subject for all conics.[31] Moreover, the preceding propositions are the foundation of the so-called "*Théorie des polaires réciproques.*"[32]

2. CONCERNING THE CENTER OF SIMILITUDE

§ 11

If in a plane through any point E (Fig. 13) we draw rays (lines) in all directions, EA_1, EB_1, EC_1, ..., and by means of these rays, so connect with one another all points of the plane that to every point A_1 on such a ray as EA_1 corresponds another point A_2 on the same ray; and indeed,

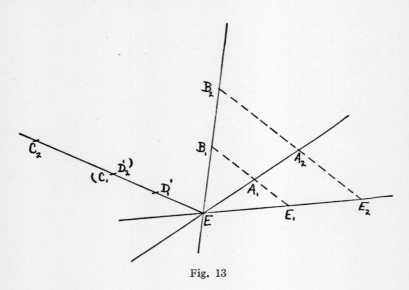

Fig. 13

under the condition that the distances of every two corresponding points from the point E, as EA_1 and EA_2, have throughout one and the same given ratio, as $n_1 : n_2$, then such a system of correspondence is thereby brought about that the plane is traversed twice. Or, we can also imagine that two planes, which may be called α and α', lie one upon the other, while every point may be considered as belonging as well in one as in the other plane. For example, the point (C_1, D_2') may be regarded as belonging to the plane α, consequently as C_1; and then the point C_2 corresponds to it. Or it may be regarded as belonging to the plane α', that is, as D_2', with D_1' corresponding to it.

If we suppose that the point A_1 moves so that it approaches the point E, the corresponding point A_2 must necessarily approach the fixed point E at the same time, until finally both coincide with E simultaneously. Accordingly, we may say that *two corresponding points are coincident at E*, and it is clear that this property can belong to this point alone (except for the special system of correspondence where the given ratio is $n_1 : n_2 = 1$, in which case every point coincides with its corresponding point).

From the simple law by which the corresponding points of the two planes α and α' are determined, there now follows directly the reciprocal relation which any system of points in the one plane has to the corresponding system of points in the other plane. That is, if in one plane any figure is given, it may be easily determined what kind of a figure corresponds to it in the other plane, and what reciprocal relation any two such corresponding figures have to each other. The chief properties or principal propositions concerning this relation depend on the following:

First of all, it is clear that the line A_1B_1, which passes through any two points A_1 and B_1 in the one plane α, is parallel to the line $A_2'B_2'$, which passes through the two corresponding points A_2' and B_2' in the other plane α'; and that the line-segments A_1B_1 and $A_2'B_2'$ of these lines, which are limited by the given points, have the same ratio to each other as the distances of any two corresponding points from the point E; that is,

$$A_1B_1 : A_2'B_2' = n_1 : n_2.$$

For, by virtue of the system of correspondence, the triangles A_1EB_1 and $A_2'EB_2'$ are evidently similar, from which the statements made follow directly. In a similar manner it follows further: that each of the two lines A_1B_1 and $A_2'B_2'$ contains all points which correspond to the points on the other line; that is, to any point on the one line, for example the point E_1 on the line A_1B_1, corresponds that point E_2'[33] on the other line $A_2'B_2'$ which lies with E_1 on the same ray passing through E; so that to every line in one plane corresponds a definite line in the other plane. As a result we have the following propositions:

I. *To every line in one plane corresponds a definite line in the other plane; i. e., to every point of each line corresponds a point of the other line. Every two such corresponding lines are parallel, and every two corresponding segments (of two such lines) are in the same ratio as the distances of any two corresponding points from the point E, that is as $n_1 : n_2$.* And conversely: *A line which passes through any two points in one plane corresponds to that line which is determined by the corresponding points in the* *other plane.* An important special case of this is the following proposition:

II. *In every line passing through E, that is in every ray, two corresponding lines are merged.*

III. *To the point of intersection of any two lines in one plane corresponds the point of intersection of their corresponding lines in the other plane.*

IV. *If we draw from any two corresponding points, as from A_1 and A_2', two parallel segments in any direction, as A_1E_1 and $A_2'E_2'$, which are in the ratio of the system of correspondence, that is, $A_1E_1:A_2'E_2' = n_1:n_2$, their other end-points E_1 and E_2' are also corresponding points and as such lie on a ray passing through E.*

From these fundamental propositions now follow the next theorems.

V. *To any rectilinear figure in one plane corresponds a similar and similarly situated figure in the other plane; that is to say, the vertices of the two figures are corresponding points so that they lie on rays by twos, and their sides are corresponding lines (or segments) and so are parallel in pairs.*

VI. *To any curved line K_1 in one plane α corresponds a similar and similarly situated curve K_2' in the other plane α'. The points in which the first curve K_1 is cut by any line g_1 correspond to the points in which the corresponding line g_2' cuts the second curve K_2', so that K_1 and g_1 intersect in just as many points as K_2' and g_2'. Therefore, to every tangent to the first curve corresponds a definite parallel tangent to the second curve, and indeed, their points of contact must also be corresponding points. Every ray passing through E which touches one curve touches the other curve also, and indeed it touches them in corresponding points,* etc.

In particular, it also follows from this that:

VII. *To any circle in one plane corresponds a circle in the other, and the centers of two such circles are also corresponding points.*

By virtue of this property of the system of correspondence the point E is called the *"center of similitude"*; or, in consideration of the fact that the two planes α and α' lie upon each other, the *"point of projection."*

With such a system of correspondence, however, two essentially different cases are to be distinguished from each other. Thus we can either:

(a) take every two corresponding points, as A_1 and A_2, on the same side of the center of similitude E, as happened in the preceding consideration; or

(b) take every two corresponding points on opposite sides of the center of similitude, in which case this point will hereafter be designated by I.[34]

These two cases are separated in what follows; in the first case we shall say that the system of correspondence has an *"external"* and in the second case an *"internal"* center of similitude.

Every two similar figures, rectilinear or curved, may be so placed that they have in one position an external and in another an internal center of similitude. There is also a certain class of figures which may at the same time satisfy both demands; that is, those which may be placed in such a position that they have at the same time an external and an internal center of similitude. If it is said of two figures in a plane that they are similar and similarly situated, they always have a center of similitude (V and VI).

§ 12

I.   From the preceding general laws concerning the center of similitude there follow for the circle in particular the properties mentioned below.

If in a plane any two *unequal, non-concentric* *circles are given, on matter what their relative positions, they always have at the same time an external and an internal center of similitude.*

Let M_1 and M_2 (Fig. 14) be the centers of the circles and A_1B_1 and A_2B_2 any two parallel diameters of the same. Then, if we draw

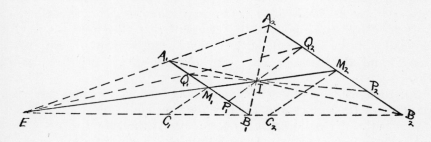

Fig. 14

through the centers the line M_1M_2, which we might call the *"axis,"* the end-points of the diameters on the same side of M_1M_2 are collinear with the external center of similitude, and those on opposite sides are collinear with the internal center of similitude. That is, the lines or rays A_1A_2 and B_1B_2 meet M_1M_2 in one and the same fixed point E, and the rays A_1B_2 and B_1A_2 meet it in the fixed point I. For evidently, by virtue of the parallelism of the diameters, the triangles EM_1A_1 and EM_2A_2, as well as the triangles IM_1A_1 and IM_2B_2, are similar. From this it follows that

$$(i)\quad EM_1:EM_2 = M_1A_1:M_2A_2$$

and

$$(ii)\quad IM_1:IM_2 = M_1A_1:M_2B_2,$$

which, as one sees, satisfies the principle of the center of similitude. For, since the ratios on the right, which are formed from the radii of the circles, remain constant, no matter what parallel direction these radii may have, the ratios on the left, that is, $EM_1:EM_2$ and $IM_1:IM_2$, must have the same constant value, as $n_1:n_2$; and therefore (since the centers M_1 and M_2 are fixed): *all lines or rays which pass through the end-points of parallel diameters lying on the same side of M_1M_2 must meet it in one and the same fixed point E, and the rays which pass through the end-points lying on opposite sides of it meet it in one and the same fixed point I; and these two fixed points are the centers of similitude of the given circles.*

Since $M_2A_2 = M_2B_2$, being radii of the circle (M_2), the two ratios on the right (in (i) and (ii)) are equal. Therefore, we have also

$$(iii)\quad EM_1:EM_2 = IM_1:IM_2;$$

i. e., *the two centers, M_1 and M_2, of the circles and their two centers of similitude, E and I, are always four harmonic points; and indeed, the two former as well as the two latter are harmonically conjugate points.*

It may be likewise noticed that the centers of the circles always lie of necessity on the same side of the external center of similitude. On the other hand, the internal center of similitude must always lie between them.

Further, we may observe the following facts concerning the relative position of the circles and their centers of similitude:

1.   If the circles lie entirely outside each other, their direct common tangents intersect at the external center of similitude E and their transverse common tangents at the internal center of similitude I, so that both centers of similitude lie outside of both circles.

2.   If we imagine the circles to approach each other or, while the centers and centers of similitude remain fixed, grow larger in the same proportion until they touch, i. e., touch *externally*, their point of contact is at the same time their *internal* center of similitude.

3.   If we move the circles further in the same manner, until they intersect, their internal center of similitude, I, lies within both circles.

4.   If the smaller circle penetrates so far into the larger that it is just tangent to it, i. e., touches it *internally*, then their point of contact is at the same time their *external* center of similitude.

5.   If the smaller circle finally arrives entirely within the larger, then both centers of similitude lie within the smaller circle.

6.   If, finally, the circles become concentric, both centers of similitude coincide with their common center.

7.   In particular, if the circles are equal to each other, no matter whether they intersect or lie exterior to each other, the internal center of similitude, I, lies midway between their centers and the external center of similitude, E, is infinitely distant.

We may be very easily convinced of the correctness of these statements by the aid of considerations set forth above.

II.   According to what precedes, the end-points of any two parallel radii of the two circles are collinear with the external or internal center of similitude, according as they lie on the same or opposite sides of M_1M_2. Therefore, the converse must of necessity also hold, namely:

If we draw through one of the two centers of similitude, E or I, of two given circles (M_1) and (M_2) any line cutting one circle, it must necessarily cut the other circle also, and that in corresponding points, so that the radii of both circles drawn to these points are parallel by twos. For example, with a line passing through E which cuts the circles (M_1) and (M_2) in B_1 and C_1, B_2 and C_2, the radii M_1B_1 and M_2B_2, as well as M_1C_1 and M_2C_2, must be parallel.

III.   Since for both systems of similitude the ratio $n_1:n_2$, by which corresponding points are determined (§ 11), is given by the radii of the circles (I) and has therefore the same value for both, and since $EM_1: EM_2$, as well as $IM_1:IM_2$, is equal to this value (I, *i* and *ii*), consequently M_1 and M_2 are simultaneously corresponding points of both systems.

If we take any point Q_1 and consider it, with respect to both systems of similitude, as belonging to the circle[35] (M_1) in the same plane α (§ 11), then in the other plane α' to which the other circle (M_2) belongs two different points will correspond to it. That is to say, a definite point Q_2[36] corresponds to it with respect to the center of similitude E and a definite point P_2 in consequence of the center of similitude I. These two points Q_2 and P_2 must, of course, lie on one and the same diameter[37] of the circle (M_2) and indeed be equally distant from its center; i. e., $Q_2M_2P_2$ must be a straight line and $Q_2M_2 = M_2P_2$. For since M_1 and M_2 are corresponding points with respect to both centers of similitude, and since, further, Q_1 and Q_2 are corresponding points with respect to E, and Q_1 and P_2 with respect to I, accordingly both M_2Q_2 and M_2P_2 are parallel to M_1Q_1 (§ 11, I). Therefore, $Q_2M_2P_2$ is a straight line, and we have the ratios

$$EM_1:EM_2 = M_1Q_1:M_2Q_2$$

and

$$IM_1:IM_2 = M_1Q_1:M_2P_2,$$

therefore (I, *iii*):

$$M_1Q_1:M_2Q_2 = M_1Q_1:M_2P_2,$$

and then:

$$M_2Q_2 = M_2P_2.$$

Consequently: *To any point which is considered as belonging to one circle, as the point Q_1 to the circle (M_1), correspond, by virtue of the two centers of similitude E and I, with respect to the other circle (M_2) two points Q_2 and P_2 such that they lie on one and the same diameter of this circle and are equidistant from its center, on opposite sides. Only the centers M_1 and M_2 of the two circles have the property that they are simultaneously corresponding points with respect to the two centers of similitude.*

According to this, if one circle (M_2) is drawn but the other (M_1) is not, and if the centers of similitude E and I are given, then to any point Q_2 or P_2, regarded as belonging to (M_2), we can easily find the corresponding point belonging to (M_1) taken with respect to the external or to the internal center of similitude. For, draw the straight line $Q_2M_2P_2$ and take the point P_2 or Q_2 so that $Q_2M_2 = M_2P_2$ (which, under the supposition that the circle (M_2) is given, may be easily done), and draw the lines EQ_2 and IP_2. Then these will intersect in the desired point Q_1. If we draw the lines EP_2 and IQ_2, they will intersect in a point P_1 which is also a corresponding point. Then $Q_1M_1P_1$ is a straight line and $Q_1M_1 = M_1P_1$. The points easiest to find are those that lie on the circumference of the circle, because for this case in every diameter of the given circle two equal segments are given at once; as, for example, *in the diameter A_2B_2 the segments A_2M_2 and M_2B_2, from which immediately, according to the manner just indicated, the end-points A_1 and B_1 of the corresponding diameter of the other circle are found.* This last construction finds frequent application in the problems following below (§ 18).

From the preceding statement we easily deduce further: *That to every line that belongs to one circle, as, for example, any line g_1 which we may regard as belonging to the circle (M_1), correspond with respect to the two centers of similitude E and I two distinct lines g_2 and h_2 belonging to the circle (M_2), which are parallel to each other (because each is parallel to g_1) and are equidistant from the center M_2.* In particular, if the line g_1 passes through the center M_1 of the circle to which it belongs, the two lines g_2 and h_2 coincide and pass through the center M_2 of the circle to which they belong.   And, finally, if g_1 coincides with M_1M_2, g_2 and h_2 will also coincide with it.[†,38]

† From the great throng of applications, which may be deduced from the properties of the center of similitude and which I shall develop in detail in another place, I shall here briefly indicate only one example which explains in a peculiar way the connection of some frequently considered, remarkable points of the rectilinear triangle.   The example is the following:

I. If in any triangle ABC (Fig. 15) we draw line-segments AA_1, BB_1, CC_1 from the vertices to the midpoints, A_1, B_1, C_1, of the opposite sides, these segments intersect in one and the

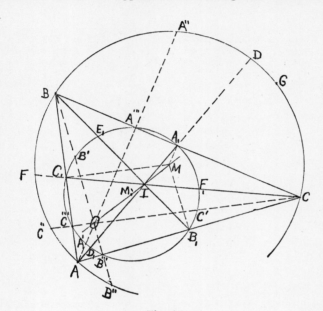

Fig. 15

same point I, as is well known, and divide one another in such manner that the parts cut off on each are in the ratio of $2:1$, i. e., we have the ratios

$$(1) \quad IA:IA_1=IB:IB_1=IC:IC_1=2:1.$$

From this it follows that we may regard the point I as the center of similitude (or pole of projection) of a system of correspondence, in which A and A_1, B and B_1, C and C_1 are corresponding points, so that A, B, C belong in one plane α and A_1, B_1, C_1 in the other plane α'; or, in a word, that the triangles ABC and $A_1B_1C_1$ are corresponding triangles, and that every two similarly situated points with respect to these traingles are at the same time similarly situated points with respect to the center of similitude I; that is, they are collinear with I and are distant from it in the constant ratio $2:1$ (§ 11).

If now it is further supposed known that the three perpendiculars A_1M, B_1M, C_1M erected at the midpoints A_1, B_1, C_1 of the sides of the first triangle ABC to these sides meet in a point M, the center of the circumscribed circle, and if we notice that these same lines are also perpendicular to the corresponding sides of the second triangle $A_1B_1C_1$ (because these are parallel, respectively, to the sides of the first), then it follows directly, if we consider the perpendiculars, for a moment, as belonging to the triangle $A_1B_1C_1$, because of the center of similitude I, that also the three lines corresponding to them, i. e., the lines AO, BO, CO drawn through the vertices A, B, C of the first triangle parallel to those perpendiculars and therefore perpendicular to the opposite sides of this triangle, meet one another in a definite

For the sake of what follows it is expedient to give definite names to the elements here considered. Any two corresponding points, as Q_1 and Q_2, or Q_1 and P_2, are to be called hereafter *"similarly situated"*

point O, and indeed in that point which corresponds to the point M. Accordingly, the three points M, I, and O lie in a straight line (ray of projection) and we have the proportion:

$$(2) \quad IO:IM=2:1.$$

From these considerations follows immediately, first of all, and in two ways, the well-known theorem: *"That the perpendiculars (A_1M, B_1M, C_1M or AO, BO, CO) dropped from the vertices upon the opposite sides of a triangle ($A_1B_1C_1$ or ABC) always meet in one and the same point (M or O)."*

It further follows, if we regard the point M as belonging to the first plane α and indeed as the center of the circle circumscribed about the triangle ABC, that to it then corresponds the center M_1 of the circle circumscribing the triangle $A_1B_1C_1$; and that consequently, this last point M_1 must likewise lie on the aforementioned ray MIO; and indeed must lie so that we have the following proportion:

$$(3) \quad IM:IM_1=2:1.$$

From this and the preceding relation (2) it follows, as we see from the figure, that we also have the proportion:

$$(4) \quad OM:OM_1=2:1,$$

so that the point O is obviously the external center of similitude of the two circles (M) and (M_1).

Accordingly, taking these results together, we have the following theorem:

In the case of any triangle ABC the two points O and I, O being the intersection of the three altitudes and I the intersection of the three lines drawn from the vertices to the midpoints of the opposite sides, always lie in one and the same straight line with the centers M and M_1 of the two circles, one of which is circumscribed about the triangle and the other of which passes through the midpoints of the sides. Indeed, the two first-named points are the centers of similitude of the two circles, so that the four points indicated are harmonic (§ 12, I), the first pair as well as the second pair being harmonically conjugate points. And further, the distances of the four points from one another are so related that we have the proportion:

$$(5) \quad IM_1:IM:OM_1:OM=1:2:3:6.$$

II. By virtue of the circles (M) and (M_1) and their centers of similitude O and I, we deduce directly other properties, as, for example, the following:

(1) The segments OA, OB, OC in α correspond with respect to the internal center of similitude I to the segments MA_1, MB_1, MC_1 in α'; therefore we have the proportion:

$$OA:MA_1 = OB:MB_1 = OC:MC_1 = 2:1.$$

(2) The points A', B', C', in which the circle (M_1) cuts the rays OA, OB, OC, are by virtue of the external center of similitude O the midpoints of these rays, so that we have the proportion:

$$OA:OA' = OB:OB' = OC:OC' = 2:1.$$

(3) If we denote the points in which the circles (M) and (M_1) are cut by the three rays AA_1, BB_1, CC_1, passing through their internal center of similitude I, by D and D_1, E and E_1, F and F_1, respectively, then we have the proportion:

$$ID:ID_1 = IE:IE_1 = IF:IF_1 = 2:1.$$

(4) Since the point M_1 lies midway between M and O (I, 4), and since MA_1 and OA''' are perpendicular to A_1A''', the circle (M_1) must pass also through A''', because it passes through A_1; and in the same way it must pass through B''' and C'''. Or the same result follows from the fact that M_1A_1 is parallel to MA, with respect to I; and that M_1A' is parallel to MA, with respect to O; that therefore A_1M_1A' is a diameter of the circle (M_1); and consequently that $A_1A'''A'$ is a right angle inscribed in a semicircle; etc.

(5) If the rays OA''', OB''', OC''' are produced until they cut the first circle (M) in A'', B'', and C'', then with respect to O we have the proportion:

$$OA'':OA''' = OB'':OB''' = OC'':OC''' = 2:1.$$

points" with respect to the two circles (M_1) and (M_2) to which they belong. In the same way two lines, which with respect to one of the two systems of correspondence are corresponding lines, are called *"similarly*

(6) Considering the circle (M_1), it now follows further, (4) and (§ 17), that

$$\text{rectangle } AB_1 \cdot AB''' = \text{rectangle } AC_1 \cdot AC''',$$
$$\text{rectangle } BA_1 \cdot BA''' = \text{rectangle } BC_1 \cdot BC''',$$

and

$$\text{rectangle } CA_1 \cdot CA''' = \text{rectangle } CB_1 \cdot CB'''.$$

(7) With respect to the center of similitude O, it now follows (§ 17) that

$$\text{rectangle } OA \cdot OA''' = \text{rectangle } OB \cdot OB''' = \text{rectangle } OC \cdot OC''' =$$
$$\text{rectangle } OA'' \cdot OA' = \text{rectangle } OB'' \cdot OB' = \text{rectangle } OC'' \cdot OC';$$

and with respect to I, it follows that

$$\text{rectangle } IA \cdot ID_1 = \text{rectangle } IB \cdot IE_1 = \text{rectangle } IC \cdot IF_1 =$$
$$\text{rectangle } ID \cdot IA_1 = \text{rectangle } IE \cdot IB_1 = \text{rectangle } IF \cdot IC_1.$$

These preceding statements (1 to 7) may be easily expressed in words in the usual way, as for example, the following theorem:

In every triangle ABC there are twelve points that lie on the circle (M_1)—namely, the three midpoints A_1, B_1, C_1 of the sides, the three feet of the altitudes A''', B''', C''', the three midpoints A', B', C' of those segments of the altitudes included between O their point of intersection and the vertices of the triangle, and finally the three points D_1, E_1, F_1 lying on the medians and are half as far from their common point of intersection I as are the points D, E, F in which the same lines cut the circumscribed circle (M), but not on the same side of the point I as the latter. And so on.

III. As a consequence of the above remark (I) that similarly situated points with respect to the triangles ABC and $A_1B_1C_1$ are also similarly situated points with respect to the center of similitude I, we may add that if we consider the four circles to which each of the three sides (or the sides produced) of the triangle ABC is tangent and also the four circles similarly related to the second triangle $A_1B_1C_1$; that then each of the last four corresponds to one of the first four. That is, these circles then have by twos the point I for an internal center of similitude, and their centers lie by twos on rays passing through this point, and the distances of their centers from I have the ratio 2:1. This is also true of the triangles ABC and $A'B'C'$ with respect to their center of similitude O.—The triangles $A'B'C'$ and $A_1B_1C_1$ are equal and M_1 is their (internal) center of similitude, because A_1M_1A' is a straight line and M_1 lies midway between A_1 and A'. And so forth.

IV. *If on the circumference of a circle (M) we take any four points A, B, C, G, then these taken three at a time determine four triangles to which belongs in common the point M, as center of the circumscribed circle, contrasted with which, however, there belongs to the same four distinct points I, as well as four M_1-points, and four O-points. Each four of these points taken separately lie on a circle. The radii of these three new circles are by turns $1/3$, $1/2$, $1/1$ of the radius of the given circle (M); and their centers are collinear with its center, and are indeed at such distances from the same that we have in turn the proportion as $2:3:6$. Then the point M is the common center of similitude of the three new circles. And further: If we join every one of the four given points A, B, C, G, as G, with the point O belonging to the other three (i. e., with the point of intersection of the altitudes of the triangle determined by the other three) by a line, then the four lines formed in this manner intersect in one and the same point, and each is bisected at this point. And so forth.*

V. I have already indicated in another place the most essential of the preceding theorems, namely on the occasion of the paper: "Développement d'une série de théorèmes relatifs aux sections coniques," in the *Annales de Mathématiques*, rédigées par GERGONNE, à Montpellier, tome XIX, 1828. In the very same place I also pointed out the theorem: *That the circle (M_1) is tangent to all four circles which can be inscribed in the triangle ABC*, without knowing that the same had been made known before this by FEUERBACH. Moreover, Professor DOVE has deduced in a simple manner the relation between the four points in (I, 5) as well as the property (II, 4) by the direct reference of the two triangles ABC and $A_1B_1C_1$ to each other, without the use of the center of similitude.[38]

situated lines" with respect to the circles. Finally, every ray which
passes through one of the two centers of similitude E or I is called a
"*line of similitude*" (or "*line of projection*") with respect to the circles.

§ 13

I. If we consider any three circles in a plane, whose centers M_1,
M_2, M_3, (Fig. 16)[39] are not collinear, then to every two of these belong
two centers of similitude, one external and one internal (§ 12). Let E_3
and I_3, E_2 and I_2, E_1 and I_1 be the centers of similitude relative to the
pairs of circles (M_1) and (M_2), (M_1) and (M_3), (M_2) and (M_3). These
six centers of similitude lie by threes on four straight lines; that is to
say, the three external centers are collinear, and each external center is
collinear with the two internal centers not belonging to it; that is,

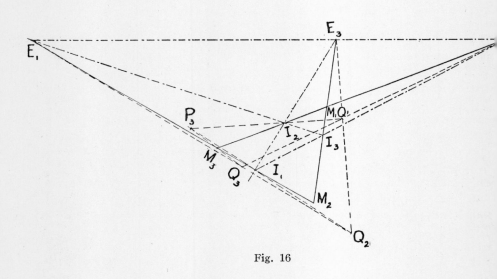

Fig. 16

$E_3E_2E_1$, as well as $E_3I_2I_1$, and $E_2I_1I_3$, and $E_1I_2I_3$, is a straight line. For if
we draw, for example, the line E_3E_2, it is because of the points E_3 and
E_2 an external line of similitude to the circles (M_1) and (M_2) as well as to
the circles (M_1) and (M_3). Therefore, it must also be an external line
of similitude of the circles (M_2) and (M_3), and as such must go through
their external center of similitude E_1. Or, to convince ourselves of this

ocularly, imagine parallel lines M_1N_1, M_2N_2, and M_3N_3 drawn from the centers M_1, M_2, and M_3 of the circles in any direction to cut the line E_3E_2. These have the ratio of the radii of the circles with respect to the centers of similitude E_3 and E_2. Then if the radii be represented by r_1, r_2, and r_3, we have:

$$M_1N_1 : M_2N_2 = r_1 : r_2 \text{ (with respect to } E_3 \text{)},$$
$$M_1N_1 : M_3N_3 = r_1 : r_3 \text{ (with respect to } E_2 \text{)};$$

consequently

$$M_2N_2 : M_3N_3 = r_2 : r_3,$$

from which it follows (§ 11, IV) that the line N_2N_3 or E_3E_2 passes through the center of similitude E_1 of the circles (M_2) and (M_3).

In the same way the other three cases follow. Then:

1. *The six centers of similitude which belong to any three coplanar circles, taken by twos, lie by threes on four straight lines; for the three external centers are collinear and each external center is collinear with the two internal centers not belonging to it;* or in other words: *the three circles have four common lines of similitude, one external and three internal.*[40]

2. If, in particular, the three circles are external to one another, their common tangents intersect in their six centers of similitude (§ 12, I, 1); so that then the preceding theorem may be interpreted 'n connection with the intersections of the six pairs of tangents which the circles taken by twos have in common.

3. If, in particular, one circle (M_3) is tangent to the other two, the two points of contact are at the same time either (§ 12, I, 2 and 4) (i) the centers of similitude E_1 and E_2, or I_1 and I_2, or (ii) the centers of similitude E_1 and I_2, or E_2 and I_1; according as it is tangent (i) in the same way to both circles, or (ii) in different ways, that is, tangent externally to one and internally to the other. Therefore we may say (1): *If any two circles (M_1) and (M_2) are tangent to some third circle (M_3), the two points of tangency are always collinear with their external center of similitude E_3, or internal center of similitude I_3, according as they are touched in the same way or in different ways by the third circle.*[41]

4. If, further in particular, two circles are equal to each other, as $r_1 = r_3$, then their internal center of similitude I_2 lies midway between their centers M_1 and M_3 and their external center of similitude E_2 is infinitely distant (§ 12, I, 7) so that the axes of similitude $I_1I_3[E_2]$ and $E_1E_3[E_2]$ are necessarily parallel to the line M_1M_3. If all three circles are equal to one another, the axis of similitude $E_1E_3E_2$ becomes infinitely distant, and the three internal axes of similitude I_1I_2, I_2I_3, I_3I_1 are parallel to the lines M_1M_2, M_2M_3, M_3M_1.

II.   Concerning the three circles considered only one further remark with respect to the centers of similitude is to be added.   If Q_1 and Q_2 are any two similarly situated points of the circles (M_1) and (M_2) with respect to their external center of similitude E_3, then the rays E_2Q_1 and E_1Q_2 will intersect in that point Q_3 which corresponds to these two points with respect to the centers of similitude E_2 and E_1.   That is, Q_1 and Q_3, Q_2 and Q_3 are similarly situated points of the circles (M_1) and (M_3), (M_2) and (M_3), respectively.   In the same way the rays I_2Q_1 and I_1Q_2 will intersect in that point P_3 which corresponds to the two points Q_1 and Q_2 with respect to the centers of similitude I_2 and I_1.   The two points Q_3 and P_3, however, will always lie on a diameter, $*$[or on a diameter produced]$_*$, of the third circle (M_3) and at equal distances from its center.   From the foregoing one may readily convince himself of the correctness of these properties.

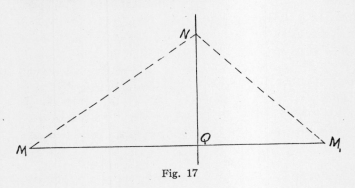

Fig. 17

3.   Power with Respect to Circles[42]

A.   The Locus of $*$Points with$_*$ Equal Powers

§14

If in a plane there are given any two fixed points M and M_1 (Fig. 17),[43] and there is to be found the locus of that point N for which the difference of the squares of its distances from the two fixed points is a given quantity, u^2 say, so that then

$$MN^2 - M_1N^2 = u^2,$$

then the locus in question is evidently a straight line NQ, perpendicular to the line MM_1 through the two fixed points, and cutting it in such manner that the difference of the squares of its segments is also equal to the given quantity; that is, that we also have:

$$MQ^2 - M_1Q^2 = u^2.$$

For if the point N fulfills the given condition, we have, if the perpendicular NQ is drawn from it to the line MM_1, from the right triangles NQM and NQM_1:

$$NM^2 - QM^{2\ 44} = NM_1{}^2 - QM_1{}^2 = NQ^2,$$

therefore

$$NM^2 - NM_1{}^2 = QM^2 - QM_1{}^2 = u^2.$$

Since, however, the line MM_1 can be cut only in the single point Q so that the difference of the squares of the segments, that is, $QM^2 - QM_1{}^2$, has a given value u^2, the perpendicular mentioned, NQ, meets the line MM_1 always in the very same fixed point Q. Therefore the locus of N is a fixed line NQ.[45]

Whether the point Q lies between the two fixed points M and M_1 or on the same side of them both depends on the mutual relation between the quantity u and the segment MM_1, that is, according as u is smaller or larger than MM_1.

§ 15

If circles are described with any radii r and r_1 about the points M and M_1, and it is desired to find the locus of the point N for the special case when the difference of the squares of its distances from these points equals the difference of the squares of the radii; i. e.,

$$MN^2 - M_1N^2 = r^2 - r_1{}^2 = u^2, \tag{1}$$

then, if in particular the circles intersect each other, the required line-locus NQ must necessarily be their common secant; i. e., it will pass through their mutual points of intersection. For, designating either of these two points by N, we have $MN = r$ and $M_1N = r_1$, which evidently satisfy the preceding condition for N.

If, however, the circles do not intersect each other, neither of them will be met by the line-locus NQ; but it then lies either *between* or *on the same side* of the circles, according as they lie *outside of each other* or *one within the other*.

In general the line-locus NQ is related to the two circles as follows:

(a) *The tangents drawn from any point of the locus to the circles are equal to each other;* and

(b) *The shortest chords drawn in the two circles through any point of the line which lies within the circles* (in the case, then, where these intersect each other) *are equal to each other.* And conversely:

(c) *Every point possessing one of these two properties* (a) *or* (b) *lies on the line-locus NQ.*

For, if a tangent is considered drawn to each circle from any point N of the line-locus, and if the points of tangency are called B and B_1 and if further the lines MN and M_1N as well as the radii MB and M_1B_1 are considered drawn, then by virtue of the right triangles MBN and M_1B_1N:

$$NB^2 = MN^2 - MB^2 = MN^2 - r^2 \tag{2}$$

and

$$NB_1{}^2 = M_1N^2 - M_1B_1{}^2 = M_1N^2 - r_1{}^2. \tag{3}$$

Because of equation (1), however, the differences on the right of (2) and (3) are equal to each other. Consequently we have also

$$NB^2 = NB_1{}^2,$$

or

$$NB = NB_1.$$

That is, the tangents must be equal to each other (a). In a similar way the second case (b) is demonstrated.

On account of this property, the line-locus NQ is called *"the line of equal powers"*; or also, with respect to its points which lie outside the circles, *"the line of equal tangents"* of the two circles. Concerning the real reasons for the first name, the reader should see the above-mentioned (§ 2) memoir (in *Journal für Mathematik*)[46], where this matter is treated in somewhat greater detail.

If, in particular, the circles touch each other, the line of equal powers is at the same time their common tangent at their point of contact.

§ 16

If we consider any three coplanar circles $(M_1), (M_2), (M_3)$ whose centers are not collinear, then every two of the circles have a line of equal powers. Let N_3Q_3, N_2Q_2, N_1Q_1 be, respectively, the lines of equal powers of the circles (M_1) and (M_2), (M_1) and (M_3), (M_2) and (M_3).

The point Q, in which two of the three lines of equal powers such as the lines N_3Q_3 and N_2Q_2 intersect, has equal powers with respect to the circles (M_1) and (M_2) because of the line N_3Q_3 and with respect to the circles (M_1) and (M_3) because of the line N_2Q_2. That is, if the point Q lies outside the circles, the tangents drawn from it to the circles (M_1) and (M_2), as well as those drawn to the circles (M_1) and (M_3), are equal to one another. Then tangent $QB_1 =$ tangent QB_2 and tangent $QB_1 =$ tangent QB_3. If Q lies within the circles, the shortest chords passing through it of the circles (M_1) and (M_2), as well as those of circles (M_1)

and (M_3), are equal to each other.   Consequently it has equal powers, also, with respect to the circles (M_2) and (M_3) (that is, the tangents drawn from it to these circles, or the shortest chords of these circles passing through it, are equal to each other, namely tangent $QB_2 =$ tangent QB_3).   Therefore Q lies on the third line-locus N_1Q_1 belonging to these circles.   By virtue of this property the point Q is called "*the point of equal powers of the three circles.*"

From these considerations the following theorems result:

(a) *The three lines of equal powers N_3Q_3, N_2Q_2, N_1Q_1 belonging to any three coplanar circles, taken in pairs always meet in a point Q, which is the point of equal powers of all three circles.*[47]   And in particular:

(b) *If three coplanar circles intersect, taken in pairs their three common secants (or chords) always intersect in some point Q* (§ 15).

(c) *If three coplanar circles touch one another, the tangents drawn to them at the points of tangency meet in a point Q.*

If the three circles intersect in a point, this is evidently at the same time their point of equal powers, Q.

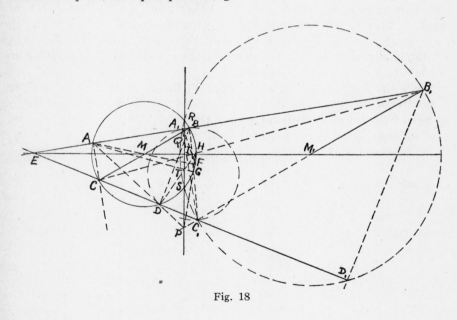

Fig. 18

B.   Joint Power

§ 17

I.   If there is drawn from one of the two centers of similitude of two circles (M) and (M_1) (Fig. 18), as from the external center of similitude

E, any line EB_1 cutting the circles, then of the four points of intersection there are two pairs, A and A_1, B and B_1, of similarly situated points (§ 12, III). The two points of intersection for one circle, however, may be grouped in another order in pairs with those for the other, namely A and B_1, B and A_1. Each of these two pairs is called provisionally a pair of *dissimilarly situated points*. If now further through the same center of similitude E there be drawn any second line ED_1 cutting the circles, then in the same way there lie on it two pairs of dissimilarly situated points, namely C and D_1, D and C_1. It may easily be shown that each of these pairs of points lies on some circle with each pair of dissimilarly situated points of the first line. Then the four points A, B_1, and C, D_1 are cyclic; so also are A, B_1, and D, C_1; B, A_1, and C, D_1; B, A_1, and D, C_1.

Draw, for example, the chords AC, BD, and A_1C_1. Then AC and A_1C_1, being corresponding or similarly situated lines, are parallel (§ 11, I and § 12, III). Consequently the angles of the two quadrilaterals $ABDC$ and A_1BDC_1 must be equal in pairs, and therefore, since the former is inscribed in a circle (M), the other must also be inscribed in a circle. That is, the four points A_1, B, D, and C_1 must lie on one and the same circle. So also, since the chords BC and B_1C_1 are parallel, being similarly situated lines, it follows that the quadrilateral ADC_1B_1 is inscribed in a circle. And so forth.

Since the four points B, D, A_1, and C_1 lie on a circle, then with respect to the secants EB and EC_1 because of a well-known theorem (the power of the point E with respect to the circle BA_1DC_1, see the aforesaid memoir, § 15) there follows:

$$EB \cdot EA_1 = ED \cdot EC_1;$$

similarly, since A, D, C_1, and B_1 lie on a circle,

$$EA \cdot EB_1 = ED \cdot EC_1;$$

and for similar reasons it follows that:

$$EA \cdot EB_1 = EC \cdot ED_1$$

and

$$EB \cdot EA_1 = EC \cdot ED_1.$$

Consequently, taken together:

$$EA \cdot EB_1 = EB \cdot EA_1 = EC \cdot ED_1 = ED \cdot EC_1.$$

Since these equations always hold, whatever the direction of the intersecting lines EB_1 and ED_1 (always hold then, while, for example, the ray EB_1 is rotated about the fixed center of similitude E; and since the same obtains for the internal center of similitude I), the following theorem results:

If there are drawn from one of the two centers of similitude of any two circles (M) and (M_1) any rays cutting the circles, then every two pairs of dissimilarly situated points of intersection which belong to any two separate rays are always cyclic; and further: *the rectangle of the distances of every two dissimilarly situated points from that center of similitude is of constant area, i. e., for all rays or for all pairs of points this rectangle has one and the same definite area.*

This constant area of all rectangles is called the *"joint power"* of the circles (M) and (M_1) with respect to the center of similitude in question; namely *"external"* or *"internal"* joint power, according as this center of similitude is external, E, or internal, I. Further, every two dissimilarly situated points by which a rectangle is determined, as A and B_1, are called *"power"* points.[48] (Power points need not, however, lie on the given circles themselves, only on one ray and indeed so that the rectangle of their distances from the center of similitude has the definite constant area and so that they lie on *the same* side or on *opposite* sides of the center of similitude according as this center is E or I.)

II. For problems coming later, it is important to call attention here to the following facts.

Since, of course, the four points B, A_1, D, and C_1 lie on a circle, the chords BD and A_1C_1, being common chords of this circle and of the given circles (M) and (M_1), must meet in some point Q of the common chord RS of the latter circles (§ 16, b). For similar reasons the chords (or secants) AC and B_1D_1, AD and B_1C_1, BC and A_1D_1 must meet each other on the common chord (or secant) RS of the given circles (M) and (M_1). Corresponding relations hold with respect to the internal center of similitude I. Consequently:

Two pairs of power points lying on the circles (but not on the same ray) will determine two chords limited by these circles and intersections in some point of their common chord.

Chapter III

SOLUTION OF ALL GEOMETRICAL PROBLEMS BY MEANS OF THE RULER, WHEN A FIXED CIRCLE* AND ITS CENTER* ARE GIVEN

§ 18

I. Because of the considerations concerning properties of figures contained in the two preceding chapters, we are now in a position to satisfy the real aim of this publication, namely the demand: *to solve all geometrical problems by means of the ruler alone, if any fixed circle is given in the plane.* And indeed, as was already noted at the beginning (§ 1), it amounts essentially to solving simply the following eight problems. I shall briefly indicate the principles of demonstration, on which the correctness of the constructions employed for the solution of these problems depends, if they are included in the preceding theorems; but I shall pass them over in silence, if they consist in easy, commonly known, elementary theorems.

II. Let us suppose then that any circle is drawn in the plane, as well as its center which is hereafter to be indicated by M, and that the use of the ruler is permitted only for the drawing of lines between given points; in this connection it is, however, justifiable to regard the intersection points of the auxiliary circle (M) and any line as directly given. The problems under discussion may then be solved as follows.

FIRST PROBLEM

Draw through any point a parallel to a given line,

(a) *If the given line passes through the center of the auxiliary circle, as AMB* (Fig. 19).

In this case three points on the line are directly given, namely the two points A and B where it cuts the circle and the center of the circle (M), so that one of them M lies midway between the other two. Consequently, by means of these a parallel to AB may immediately be drawn, through any point according to (§ 6, I).

(b) *If the given line cuts the auxiliary circle, but does not pass through its center, as CD.*

Draw from the points of intersection C and D through the center M the diameters of the circle, CMC_1 and DMD_1. Then their other endpoints, C_1 and D_1, determine a chord C_1D_1, which is parallel to the given *CD;* and by its help the problem may be solved at once (§ 6, III).

(c) *If the given line has any position, as the line EF.*[49]

1. Draw from any point of the given line, as from G, the diameter ABG. Draw through any point C of the circumference of the circle the chord CDE parallel to AB (a). Draw at once the diameters CMC_1 and DMD_1, and through their end-points C_1 and D_1 the line D_1C_1F. Then there are on the given line three points E, G, and F with G equally distant from the other two; so that through any point a parallel to this line can at once be drawn (§ 6, I).—Or 2. Draw from any two points H and I of the given line the diameters HC_1C and IDD_1. Through their end-points draw the parallel chords CDE and D_1C_1F, meeting the line in the points E and F. From these points draw further the diameters EME_1 and FMF_1, meeting these chords in E_1 and F_1. Then the line E_1F_1 will be parallel to the given line $EF;$ and through any point a parallel to the latter can be drawn at once (§ 6, III).

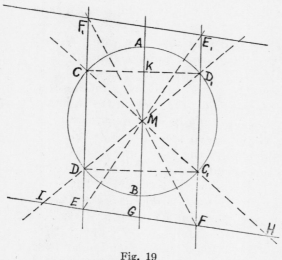

Fig. 19

NOTE: 1. The third case (c) is general. It includes also the two preceding cases, as well as the particular case when the given line is tangent to the circle.

2. If parallels are to be drawn to several given lines through given points, then we proceed most expediently, if we draw any diameter AB and at once at equal distances from it two chords CD and C_1D_1 parallel to it. Then these three parallels evidently determine three points on every line (to which they do not happen to be parallel), as E, G, and F, such that G lies midway between the other two.

Second Problem

If in a line any segment is given, (a) *find another segment which is a given multiple of the first; or* (b) *divide the given segment into any given number of equal parts; or finally* (c) *find another segment which shall have any given rational ratio to the given segment.*

Draw any parallel to the given line (first problem). Then the proposed problem may be solved at once by using (§ 6, IV).

Third Problem

Through a given point draw a perpendicular to a given line.[50]

A.   By means of parallels

(a) *If the given line is any diameter of the auxiliary circle, as AB* (Fig. 19).—Draw any chord CD parallel to the given diameter AB (§ 6, I). Then draw the diameter DMD_1, and also the chord CD_1. This will be perpendicular to the given diameter AB, and will be bisected by it at the point K. In order to satisfy the problem it is therefore only necessary at once to draw through the given point a parallel to the chord CKD_1 (§ 6, I).

In particular, to find that diameter which is perpendicular to the given AB, imagine the lines AC and BD drawn (after CD has been first drawn parallel to AB). Pass through their point of intersection and through the center M a line, and this is the desired diameter. Similarly the lines AD_1 and BC_1 intersect on the desired diameter.

(b) *If the given line cuts the auxiliary circle, as CD.*—Draw the diameters CC_1 and DD_1, and then the chords CD_1 and DC_1. These last will then be perpendicular to the given line CD and therefore parallel to each other. Consequently the problem is satisfied, if through the given point a parallel is drawn to these chords (§ 6, III).

(c) *If the given line does not cut the auxiliary circle, as EF.*—Draw any chord parallel to the given line EF (first problem). Let DC_1 be such a chord. Then draw the diameters DD_1 and C_1C, and then also the chords CD and D_1C_1. These are perpendicular to the chord DC_1 and therefore also to the given line EF, and hence parallel to each other. Consequently the problem will be solved, if through the given point a parallel is drawn to the chords CD and D_1C_1 (§ 6, III).

It is easily seen that the given point may, in all three cases (a), (b), and (c), lie wherever we wish on the given line itself or outside the same.

B.   By means of harmonic properties

(a) *If the given line is a diameter of the auxiliary circle, as AB* (Fig. 20).—α. Let the given point lie outside the auxiliary circle, as P.

Draw through the point P and through the extremities of the diameter AB the lines PA and PB which cut the circle the second time in C and D, respectively.   Draw the lines AD and CB, which intersect each other in some point P_1.   Then PP_1 is the desired line.   For, since ACB and ADB are right angles, P_1C and PD are, with respect to the triangle PAP_1, two perpendiculars from the vertices to the opposite sides. Consequently, AB must be the perpendicular dropped from the third vertex to the opposite side, since all three such perpendiculars must meet in one and the same point B.   The proof follows also from harmonic properties; to this end only the additional line CSD need be drawn (§ 10).[51]—In particular, if the given point lies on the given diameter, as R, draw through it any line cutting the circle, as REF.   Draw also the lines AE and BF, AF and BE, which intersect in the points Q

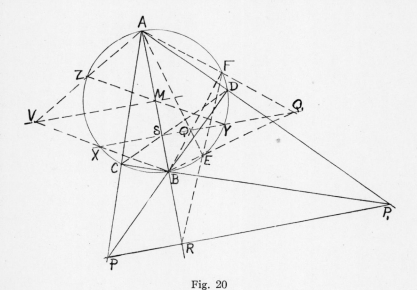

Fig. 20

and Q_1.   Pass through these the line QQ_1, meeting the given diameter AB in S.   Through this point S draw any secant CSD.   Then draw forthwith the lines AC and DB, AD and CB, intersecting in P and P_1. Finally, draw the line PP_1, which will satisfy the problem.   The correctness of this construction follows from (§ 10, III and IV); for it is to be noticed that SQQ_1 is the polar of the point R, and PRP_1 the polar of the point S, and so forth.—β.   Let the given point lie within the auxiliary circle, as Q.   Draw the lines AQ and BQ, which cut the circle in F and E, respectively.   Draw also the lines AF and BE, which intersect each other in Q_1.   Then QQ_1 is the desired line.   If S is the given point, draw through it any chord CSD, and then the lines AC and DB, AD and CB, which intersect in P and P_1, respectively.   Draw also the line PP_1, meeting the diameter AB in R.   Pass through this point any secant REF, and draw also the lines AE and BF, AF and BE, which intersect in Q and Q_1, respectively.   Then the line QQ_1 will satisfy the requirement, i. e., it will be perpendicular to the given diameter AB at the given point S.   The same reasons are applicable as for (α).

(b) *If the given line has any position; for example, let it be* PP_1 (*or* QQ_1).—Seek its pole S (or R) with respect to the auxiliary circle (§ 10, IV).   Draw the diameter passing through the same, MS (or MR).   Then this is perpendicular to the given line PP_1 (or QQ_1) at the point R (or S).   Find the polar XY of this point R and forthwith draw YMZ, and also AZ and BX intersecting in V.   Then the diameter VM will be parallel to the given line PP_1[52]; and the problem is satisfied at once,

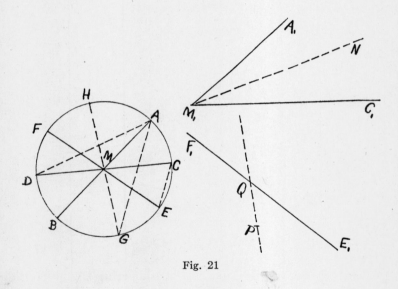

Fig. 21

by simply dropping a perpendicular upon VM from the given point, according to (a).   For the line QQ_1 the solution is somewhat simpler, as may easily be seen.

FOURTH PROBLEM

Draw a line through a given point making with a given line an angle equal to a given angle.

Let $A_1M_1C_1$ (Fig. 21) be the given angle and E_1F_1 the given line and P the given point.—Draw the diameters AB and CD parallel to the sides of the angle (first problem), so that angle AMC = angle $A_1M_1C_1$. Also, draw the diameter EF parallel to the given line E_1F_1. Then draw also the chord CE, through A the chord AG parallel to it, and further the diameter GH. Then arc AC = arc GE, and therefore angle GME = angle AMC = angle $A_1M_1C_1$. Consequently, we must finally draw through the given point P a parallel PQ to the diameter GMH (§ 6, I). Then PQE_1 ($= GME = A_1M_1C_1$) will be the desired angle. If the chord AE were drawn, instead of CE, and through C a chord parallel to it, etc., then the other angle would be obtained that also satisfies the problem and would be turned towards F_1 instead of towards E_1.

The problem is similarly solved, if in particular the given point lies on the given line E_1F_1 itself, as Q. That is, if the familiar problem is proposed:

Apply to a given line E_1F_1 at a given point Q an angle which is equal to an angle $A_1M_1C_1$[53] given in size and position.

FIFTH PROBLEM

(a) *Bisect or* (b) *multiply at will a given angle.*

Case a.[54] Let $A_1M_1C_1$ (Fig. 21) be the given angle.—Draw the diameters AB and CD parallel to the sides M_1A_1 and M_1C_1 of the angle, so that angle AMC = angle $A_1M_1C_1$. Then draw the chord AD (or CB), and through the vertex of the given angle the line M_1N parallel to AD (or CB). Then M_1N will bisect the angle $A_1M_1C_1$.

Case b. This case can be disposed of by the use of the third problem in accordance with the method of § 9. Its solution may be effected in yet another way[55] which, however, I shall omit, because it does not seem to me very fundamental.

SIXTH PROBLEM

From a given point draw a line-segment which shall be equal and parallel to a given line-segment.

Let M_1A_1 (Fig. 22) be the given line-segment and M_2 the given point. If at the same time we are to draw through M_2 many line-segments which are equal to the given segment M_1A_1, the following process appears to be the most suitable. In order that this be more easily understood, it is still to be noted first of all that the end-points of all segments satisfying the problem evidently lie on a circle (M_2) whose radius equals the given segment M_1A_1. Consequently, this leads to regarding the point M_2 and one end-point of the given segment, as M_1, as centers of two equal circles, whose radii are equal to the given segment

M_1A_1; and to finding then by the reciprocal relation of the three circles (M), (M_1), (M_2), namely by their centers of similitude, the means by which the proposed problem may be solved. To this end represent by E_2 and I_2, E_1 and I_1, E and I, respectively, the centers of similitude of the pairs of circles (M) and (M_1), (M) and (M_2), (M_1) and (M_2). Since the circles (M_1) and (M_2) are equal, their internal center of similitude I lies midway between their centers M_1 and M_2, and their external center of similitude E is infinitely distant (§ 12, I, 7). Moreover, the lines of similitude $E_1E_2[E]$ and $I_2I_1[E]$ must be parallel to the axis M_1M_2 (§ 13, I, 4). Now the proposed problem can be solved as follows.

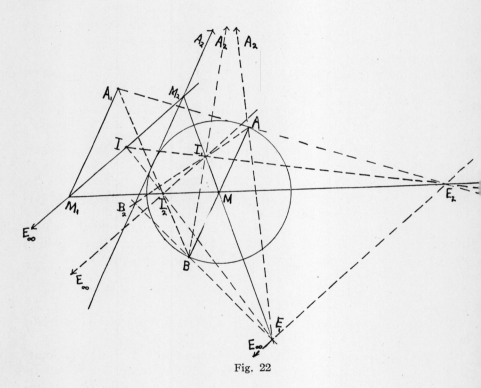

Fig. 22

Draw the lines MM_1, MM_2, and M_1M_2. Draw also the diameter AB parallel to the given segment M_1A_1, and then the lines A_1A and A_1B, cutting M_1M in E_2 and I_2, respectively. After this, proceed by passing through the point E_2, parallel to M_2M_1, the line E_2E_1, meeting M_2M in E_1. Draw also the line E_1I_2, which meets M_1M_2 in I; and draw finally the line IE_2, which cuts[56] MM_2 in I_1. Then the points E_1

and I_1 are the centers of similitude of two circles (M) and (M_2), of which the latter has as radius the given segment M_1A_1.

After these preliminaries it is now easy to draw from the point M_2 as many segments as we wish which are equal to the given segment M_1A_1. For, if there is drawn in the auxiliary circle any diameter, as, for example, AB (which, however, need not be parallel to M_1A_1), and if its extremities A and B are joined to the points E_1 and I_1 by lines E_1A and BI_1, E_1B and AI_1, then these intersect in two points A_2 and B_2, each of which is at a distance equal to the length M_1A_1 from the given point M_2; and indeed, these three points A_2, M_2, and B_2 are collinear (§ 12, III).

If, however, the direction of the segment to be drawn is given, for example, if a line is given passing through M_2 on which it is to lie, or if any line is given to which it is to be parallel, then there must first be drawn in the auxiliary circle (M) the diameter which is parallel to this line (first problem); and then the process is exactly the same as before.[57]

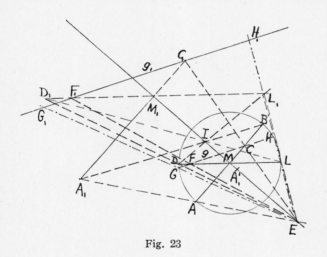

Fig. 23

SEVENTH PROBLEM

Find the points of intersection of a given line and a circle whose size and position are given (but which is not drawn).

Let g_1 (Fig. 23) be the given line, M_1 the center, and M_1A_1 the radius of the given circle.

The proposed problem can be solved by constructing the centers of similitude E and I of the two circles (M) and (M_1), and then seeking that line g which has to the auxiliary circle (M) (with respect to one or the other center of similitude) a position similar to that of the given line g_1 to the circle (M_1). For then must the points of intersection G and H of the former, g and (M), correspond to the points of intersection G_1 and H_1 of the latter, g_1 and (M_1), that is, they must be points similarly situated to them; then the required points G_1 and H_1 are found by means of the given G and H. All this, however, happens as follows.

Draw the diameter AB parallel to the given radius M_1A_1, and also the line MM_1 together with the lines A_1A and A_1B which cut MM_1 in the centers of similitude E and I (§ 12, I). Prolong the radius A_1M_1, until it meets the given line g_1 in C_1; and then draw the ray EC_1, meeting the diameter AB in C. Then C and C_1 are two similarly situated points with respect to the external center of similitude E (because AM and A_1M_1 are similarly situated lines (§ 11)). Now draw also in the auxiliary circle any diameter DL, and the lines EL, DI intersecting in L_1 (or the lines ED, LI intersecting in D_1). Draw the diameter L_1M_1 (or D_1M_1), which corresponds to DL and is therefore parallel to it, and which meets the line g_1 in F_1. Finally, draw the ray EF_1, which meets the diameter DL in F. Then F and F_1 are likewise similarly situated points with respect to the external center of similitude E. Consequently, the lines LF and L_1F_1, and the lines g and g_1, are similarly situated (§ 11, I) with respect to E; and the same is true of the points G and G_1, H and H_1 in which g and g_1 cut the corresponding circles, (M) and (M_1). Accordingly, if the line CF[58] is also drawn, cutting the circle (M) in G and H, and then the rays EG and EH, these meet the given line g_1 in the points G_1 and H_1 demanded by the problem.

NOTE: 1. With regard to the relative positions of the circle (M) and the line g three cases are possible: namely, either (1) they intersect in two points, or (2) they are tangent, or (3) they do not meet at all. In each of these three cases the same relation obtains with respect to the positions of the given circle (M_1) and given line g_1.

2. If the radius M_1A_1 were by chance parallel to the given line g_1, the point C_1 would be infinitely distant; and then it would be more convenient to use in its place some other point in the construction, which indeed would be introduced and employed in the same way as the point F_1. In practical applications it would be convenient, to employ another point instead of C_2 also in the case that the point C_1 simply lay very distant, i. e., if the lines A_1M_1 and g_1 formed a very small angle with each other.

3. Just as the line g, or chord GH, necessary for the solution of the problem, has been constructed by the aid of the external center of similitude E, so also a line h (corresponding to the given line g_1 with respect to the internal center of similitude I) may be obtained by means of

I. Then by means of two rays passing through I (and through the points of intersection of h and the auxiliary circle (M), which indeed are the other extremities of the diameters of the circle (M) passing through G and H (§ 12, III)) the same desired points G_1 and H_1 as before may be found. In a practical case therefore, as in surveying, if, for example, the given line g_1 were not everywhere accessible by reason of obstacles, but if it were given only by two points as C_1 and F_1 which lay so that one could not look from one to the other, then both centers of similitude E and I would be used at the same time, in the manner suggested, in order to obtain each of the two desired points G_1 and H_1 as a point of intersection of two rays, of which one passed through E and the other through I. In this case, however, the progress of the solution must be somewhat changed. For the diameters C_1M_1 and F_1M_1 through the given points C_1 and F_1 would first be drawn, and then the diameters AB and DL parallel to these; and from that point on the procedure would be the same as before.

4. If the given radius M_1A_1 lay, in particular, on the line MM_1, for example, if it were $M_1A'_1$,[59] how would one then have to proceed with the solution? A similar special case may come up in the preceding problem, if namely the given segment M_1A_1 lies in the direction of any diameter of the auxiliary circle (M); and the same may be considered also in the following (eighth) problem. The solution of these special cases is left as an exercise for lovers of the subject.

Eighth Problem

Find the points of intersection of two given circles.

First case. If one circle is drawn, namely the auxiliary circle (M) itself, and of the other circle only the size and position are given. Let M_1, for example, be the center (Fig. 18, p. 49,) and M_1B_1 the given radius of the second circle.

The solution of this case evidently reduces to finding the common secant of the two circles, because this then gives directly the desired points R and S on the auxiliary circle. This may be done among other ways as follows, by the use of (§ 17).

In the auxiliary circle (M) draw the diameter BC parallel to the given radius M_1B_1. Draw also the line MM_1 and the lines B_1B and B_1C, which meet it in the centers of similitude E and I, respectively, and cut (M) the second time in A and H. Now draw also the ray EC, which meets (M) the second time in D and meets the radius B_1M_1 produced in C_1. This last point lies also on the circle (M_1). Then further draw the diameter AF and forthwith the line FI which meets the ray EB_1 in the point A_1 which also belongs to the circle (M_1) (§ 12, III). Then the two points A and B_1, as well as B and A_1, and D and C_1 are power points with respect to the center of similitude E (§ 17, I). Draw further, therefore, the two pairs of chords AD and B_1C_1 (produce these), BD and A_1C_1, which intersect in P and Q. Finally, draw the line PQ. This is the common secant of the given circles (§ 17, II), and cuts the auxiliary circle (M) in the points R and S demanded by the problem.

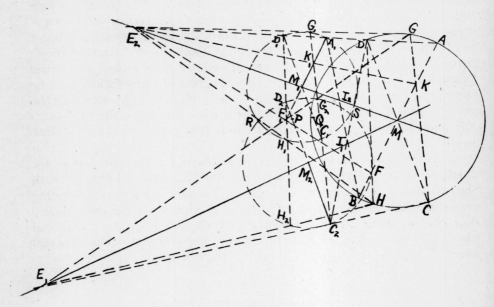

Fig. 24

NOTE: 1. If besides the supposed limits to aids in our work the further condition were added that no point of the circle (M_1) save B_1 (and the center M_1) be used, if, *e.g.*, this condition were imposed by some existing obstacles,[60] the problem might be satisfied by means of the other circle (M) alone as follows. After the centers of similitude E and I, as well as the intersections A and H, had been found in the same way as before by means of the lines B_1B and B_1C, there should be found by means of the ray EC the point D, and by means of the ray BI the point G. Then by means of the chords AD and HG the point P should be obtained and by means of the chords AG and DH the point T. Then these points P and T would lie on the common secant RS of the two given circles (M) and (M_1). The reasons, on which the accuracy of this process depends, are easy to find (Chapter II).

2. If the line found, PQ, is only tangent to the circle (M) or does

not meet it at all, this indicates that the circle (M_1) also is tangent to it or does not meet it at all.

Second case. If both circles are given only by their size and position. Let M_1 and M_2 (Fig. 24), for example, be the centers and M_1A_1 and M_2C_2 the radii of the two given circles.

This case may be solved in the following way among others, by constructing the common secant of the two given circles and then seeking the intersections of this secant and one of the two circles. This may be done, for example, as follows.

In the auxiliary circle (M) draw the diameters AB and CD parallel to the given radii M_1A_1 and M_2C_2. Then seek at once the centers of similitude E_2 and I_2, E_1 and I_1 of the pairs of circles (M) and (M_1), (M) and (M_2). Then construct with the aid of the centers of similitude E_2 and I_2 the diameter C_1D_1 of the circle (M_1) parallel to CD, and also to C_2M_2, (§ 12, III). Similarly determine the second extremity D_2 of the diameter C_2M_2. Then draw the lines C_2C_1 and D_1D_2, which cut the radius A_1M_1 in K_1 and F_1. And draw also the rays E_2K_1 and E_2F_1, which meet the diameter AMB in K and F. K and K_1, F and F_1 are similarly situated points of the circles (M) and (M_1) with respect to the center of similitude E_2. Draw further the lines CK and DF, which cut the auxiliary circle (M) (the second time) in G and H. And draw forthwith the rays E_2G and E_2H, E_1G and E_1H, which meet the lines C_2C_1 and D_1D_2, respectively, in the points G_1 and H_1, G_2 and H_2. Then these points lie on the circles (M_1) and (M_2); and indeed C_1 and G_2, as well as G_1 and C_2, and D_1 and H_2, and H_1 and D_2 are power points with respect to their external center of similitude, E. If then, further, the chords G_1H_1 and G_2H_2 are considered drawn (in order not to crowd the figure, these and some following lines are not actually drawn), and if the points in which they cut the diameters C_2D_2 and C_1D_1, respectively, are called P and Q, and if finally the line PQ is drawn, then this is the common secant of the circles (M_1) and (M_2) (§ 17, II). Thus the proposed problem is reduced to the former (seventh problem), since now in addition it is necessary to find only the points of intersection of the line PQ and one of the two circles, as the circle (M_1). This can, however, be done very easily by means of the already existent auxiliary lines. For, draw the rays E_2P and E_2Q; call the points in which they meet the chord GH and the diameter CD, respectively, P' and Q'; draw further the line $P'Q'$; call the points in which it cuts the auxiliary circle (M) R' and S', and draw finally the rays E_2R' and E_2S'. Then these will meet the line PQ in the points R and S satisfying the problem.

Several other methods of solution of the preceding problem are passed over here, because none is simpler than that just finished.   One consists, for example, in seeking the lines of equal powers (or common secants) of the pairs of circles (M) and (M_1), (M) and (M_2) (first case), and dropping a perpendicular from their point of intersection Q on the line M_1M_2.   This then is the common secant of the circles (M_1) and (M_2).   And so forth.

§ 19

CONCLUDING COMMENT

It is now easily apparent that actually all geometrical problems, taken in narrow sense, may be treated by the aid of the preceding eight problems, that is, that however complicated they may seem, they may be solved by a simple or complex combination or repetition of the operations used in the solution of the above eight problems.   Hence the aim of this treatise may be regarded as attained.   The possibility of this treatment is based particularly on the preceding *seventh* and *eighth* problems;   since indeed, as was already noted in the introduction, in ordinary geometry the majority, and the hardest, of the problems are solved by means of these two only.   However, if one wished actually to solve all geometrical problems according to the present method, and indeed in the simplest possible manner, he would naturally not follow step by step with complicated constructions the process generally employed if the free use of both instruments, ruler and compasses, is allowed;   but he would have to deliberate much more on the matter in making the solutions as simple and easy as possible with the means here permitted. In this respect the above first six problems themselves may be regarded as fundamental examples.   Moreover, the preceding problems all together show that here also, as well as in geometry in general, we depend particularly on *investigating very carefully the properties of the dependence of figures on one another*.—In particular, I shall here only note further that, for example, in such problems as demand: "to inscribe in, or circumscribe about, a circle (M_1) whose size and position alone are given (or also a circle (M_1) determined by three conditions only) a regular polygon," we may proceed, among other ways, so that this same problem is solved first for the given auxiliary circle (M) and then the polygon obtained may be projected upon the circle (M_1) by means of the centers of similitude E and I pertaining to the circles, etc.; to this end the above constructions give sufficient guidance.

I take this opportunity to add also the following observation:

It appears that in general up to now too little care has been bestowed upon geometrical constructions.   The customary method, handed

down to us by the ancients, according to which indeed problems are regarded as solved as soon as it is indicated by what means they may be
reduced to others previously treated, is a great hindrance to the accurate, critical examination of what their complete solution requires.
Thus it happens that often in this way constructions are given, which,
if it were necessary to carry out *actually* and *exactly* all that they include, would soon be given up, since thereby one would speedily be convinced that it is a very different matter actually to carry out the constructions, i. e., with the instruments in the hand, than it is to carry
them through, if I may use the expression, simply by means of the
tongue.[61] It is indeed easy to say: I shall do that, and then that and
then this; but the difficulty, and we may say in certain cases the impossibility, of really completing constructions which are highly complicated requires us to weigh carefully in a proposed problem which of the
various processes is the simplest for the complete construction, or which
is the most suitable under special circumstances, and how much of what
the tongue utters somewhat inconsiderately is to be avoided, when it
comes to sparing all superfluous trouble, or to attaining the greatest
accuracy, or to sparing as far as possible the plane (the paper) on which
the drawing is to be made. And so forth. In a word, it would then
depend upon: *seeking theoretically or practically the way in which every
geometrical problem may be constructed most simply, most exactly, and
most surely, and indeed which is the most suitable process* (1) *in general,*
(2) *under limitations as to instruments, and* (3) *with obstructions existing in
the plane of construction.*[62] This investigation would then also include as
well the method of construction of MASCHERONI as the present method;
and then a comparison of all methods would afford exact knowledge of
the matter, and would indeed be not without interest for science. That
the preceding problems may appear somewhat long should not frighten
us away from the present method; for, as has already been said, if we
really carry out everything in ordinary geometry which is demanded for
the construction in a complicated problem, it would soon be seen that
there, too, much is not at all so simple as it appears, when the transactions are adjusted in words alone. Besides, I have already convinced
myself that by this method we can find, even for apparently difficult
problems, simple solutions that cannot be made shorter or easier by the
admission of all mathematical tools. This will be shown in the
following examples.

Appendix[63]

MISCELLANEOUS PROBLEMS, TOGETHER WITH INDICATION OF THEIR SOLUTION BY MEANS OF THE RULER, AND A FIXED CIRCLE ∗WITH ITS CENTER∗

§ 20

To show how simply many problems that appear difficult may be solved by means of the ruler alone, if some fixed circle (M) is given in the plane, I give here several additional appropriate problems. The reasons, upon which depend some of the solutions here indicated, may be found in the first part of *Systematische Entwickelung der Abhängigkeit geometrischer Gestalten von einander*, and those on which the rest depend will be developed in the later parts of the same treatise.[64] Moreover, the same treatise will contain many more problems of this kind, as in the first part particularly several have already presented themselves, all of which it seemed unnecessary to me, however, to repeat here.

With regard to the following solutions I must recommend that the reader himself always draws the pictures (figures) demanded, in case he should be particular about it, in order really to see the described constructions on the paper, according to the guidance of the solution.

PROBLEM 1

If any two triangles are given in a plane, find a third which at the same time is circumscribed about the first and inscribed in the second.[65]

Let B, B_1, and B_2 be the vertices of the first and a, a_1, and a_2 the sides, and indeed the indefinitely produced sides, of the second triangle.

Take in a an arbitrary point A, and draw the ray AB which meets the line a_1 (both being sufficiently produced) in a point A_1. Draw forthwith the ray A_1B_1, cutting a_2 in a point A_2. And finally draw the ray A_2B_2, meeting a in a point A'. Now the problem has evidently no other aim than so to determine the first point A that the last-found point A' coincides with it, because in this case the triangle AA_1A_2A' satisfies the problem. Since, however, in general this coincidence does not take place, but instead A and A' will be two points that are different but dependent on and corresponding to each other, then in a similar manner seek the points B' and C' on the line a corresponding to any two points B and C taken on the same line. Then take any point P on the

66

circumference of the auxiliary circle (M), and draw the rays PA and PA', PB and PB', PC and PC', which cut the circle (the second time) in the points A'' and A''', B'' and B''', C'' and C''', respectively. Join one of these pairs of points, for example the first, crosswise with each of the other two. That is, draw the lines $A''B'''$ and $A'''B''$, intersecting in a point P', as well as the lines $A''C'''$ and $A'''C''$, intersecting in a point Q'. Draw also the line $P'Q'$, cutting the circle (M) in general in two points R and S; and finally draw the rays PR and PS. Then these will meet the side (or line) a in the points R' and S' in which alone the vertex of the triangle to be described can actually lie, so that this is then found. Accordingly, there are in general two triangles $R'R_1R_2R'$ and $S'S_1S_2S'$, each of which satisfies the proposed problem. If, however, in particular the line $P'Q'$ is simply tangent to the circle, then there is only *one* triangle; and if it does not meet the circle at all, there is *not even one* triangle fulfilling the conditions of the problem.

Note: If any quadrilateral, or pentagon, etc., is given instead of the triangle, the problem is solved in exactly the same way.

Problem 2

Find the points of intersection of a given line and a conic (not drawn) *determined simply by:* (a) *five points, or* (b) *five tangents.*[66]

Case a. Let the line be called a and the five points of the conic be B, B_1, A, B', C.—From any two of the five points, as from B and B_1, draw rays through the other three, the rays BA and B_1A, BB' and B_1B', BC and B_1C, and designate the points in which they (sufficiently produced) meet the line a by A'' and A''', B'' and B''', C'' and C''', respectively. By means of these three pairs of points seek at once, exactly in the same way as in the case of the preceding solution (problem 1), by the use then of the auxiliary circle (M), the two points R' and S' on the line a. Then these are the desired points of intersection. If the line $P'Q'$, which is found by the further construction, does not meet the auxiliary circle (M), the given line and the conic do not intersect either. If the former are tangent, so are the latter also. In this case the points R' and S' coincide.

Case b. This case may be easily reduced to the first, since indeed by means of the ruler alone we can find the five points of tangency of the conic and the five given tangents. (*Abhängigkeit geometrischer Gestalten von einander*, part I, p. 152.)

Problem 3

Find the lines which pass through a given point and are tangent to a conic determined only by: (a) *five tangents, or* (b) *five points.*[67]

Case a.   Let B' be the given point and a', a_1, a, b, and c be the five given tangents to the conic.   Denote the points in which a' and a_1 are cut by a, b, and c by A and A_1, B and B_1, C and C_1, respectively.   Draw the rays $B'A_1$, $B'B_1$, and $B'C_1$, and designate the points in which they meet the line a' by A'', B'', and C'', respectively.   By means of the three pairs of points A and A'', B and B'', C and C'' and of the auxiliary circle (M) find (in the same way as in the two preceding problems) the two points R' and S' on the line a'.   Draw forthwith the lines $B'R'$ and $B'S'$. Then these, and indeed these alone, will satisfy the demand of the problem.   If the line $P'Q'$, which is found by later construction (see problem 1), does not cut the auxiliary circle (M), this indicates that the given point B' lies within the conic, and consequently the problem is impossible.   If the line is tangent to the circle, this shows that the point lies on the conic itself, and therefore only a single line (formed of two coincident lines) can satisfy the problem.

Case b.   This case can be reduced to the first (a) by a method corresponding to that occurring in the preceding problem, 2; details of the method are also to be found there.

PROBLEM 4

If in connection with a conic four points and a tangent are given, find the point in which the latter is touched by the conic.

I.   Let a be the given line and A, B, C, D the four given points. Draw through these points three pairs of lines, namely AB and CD, AC and BD, AD and BC, and designate the points in which they meet the line a by A_1 and A_2, B_1 and B_2, C_1 and C_2, respectively.   Then straightway seek, by the same method as in the preceding problems, the points R' and S' on the line a.   Each of these will satisfy the proposed problem; so that there are in general *two* conics, each of which passes through the four given points and is tangent to the given line.   The criteria by which we recognize whether the problem actually admits of *two* solutions, or *only one*, or *none at all* (i. e., whether it is possible to have two conics, or only one, or none at all) are the same as in the preceding problems.

II.   In order to shorten the construction somewhat, one may also proceed as follows with this problem.   Draw only two pairs of lines (I) as AB and CD, AC and BD, which meet the tangent a in the points A_1 and A_2, and B_1 and B_2.   Then draw forthwith from any point P taken on the auxiliary circle (M) (compare problem 1) the rays PA_1 and PA_2, PB_1 and PB_2, which cut the circle in A' and A'', B' and B''. Draw also the lines $A'B''$ and $B'A''$, intersecting in a point P', as well as the lines $A'B'$ and $A''B''$, intersecting in a point T'.   Then draw the line $P'T'$, which will in general cut the circle (M) in two points R and S, and finally draw the rays PR and PS. These will meet the line a in the desired points R' and S'.

PROBLEM 5

If in connection with a conic four tangents and a point are given, find the tangent touching the conic in this point.

Let a, b, c, and d be the four given tangents, and A the given point. Designate the points in which a cuts b, c, and d by A', B', and C', respectively, and the points in which d and c, d and b, and c and b intersect by A_1, B_1, C_1, respectively. Draw the rays AA_1, AB_1, AC_1, and designate the points in which they meet the tangent a by A'', B'', and C'', respectively. Then, in the same way as before, seek the points R' and S' on the line a by means of the pairs of points A' and A'', B' and B'', C' and C''. Then draw the rays AR' and AS', and each of these will satisfy the problem.—Moreover, the two points R' and S' may also be found here by the same abbreviated process used in the preceding problem (4, II), in which indeed we needed only two of the three pairs of points, as A' and A'', and B' and B''.

PROBLEM 6

If in connection with a conic three points and two tangents are given, find the points of contact of the tangents.

Call the given tangents b and c and any two of the three given points A and A'. Draw the line AA' and designate the points in which it cuts b and c by B and B'. Then seek in the same manner as above (4, II) the two points R' and S' on the line AA' (a there). Now draw also through the third given point and one of the other two, A or A', a line; and seek, in exactly the same way, the two points R_1' and S_1' on it. Then draw the four lines $R'R_1'$, $R'S_1'$, $S'R_1'$, and $S'S_1'$. Each of these will cut, in particular, the tangents b and c in points where they are tangent to one and the same conic passing through the three given points. In general the proposed problem admits, therefore, of four solutions, or there are in general four conics which have the three given points, as well as the two given tangents in common.[68] The problem is (or the conics are) impossible, if one of the pairs of points R' and S', R_1' and S_1' does not exist. This case, however, may be recognized without the preceding constructions directly from the relative positions of the five given elements. That is to say, it exists when the given points with respect to the angles formed by the tangents b, c lie in *adjacent angles* (but no two of them are collinear with the point of intersection of the tangents). Special or limiting cases arise, when either the three given points are collinear or two of them are collinear with the point of intersection of the tangents b and c. And so on.

PROBLEM 7

If in connection with a conic three tangents and two points are given, find the tangents at the given points.

Call the three given tangents b, c, and d, and the two given points A and A', and further designate the points of intersection of the pairs of tangents b and c, b and d, and c and d by D, C, and B, respectively. Draw the line AA', and call the points in which it cuts the pair of tangents, as b and c, B' and B''. Then seek on the line AA' the pair of points R' and S' (4, II) determined by the pairs of points A and A', B' and B''. In a similar way seek the pair of points R_1' and S_1' determined by the given pair of points A and A' and by the pair of points in which the line AA' is cut by another pair of tangents, as by b and d. Then draw the rays DR' and DS', CR_1' and CS_1'; and denote the points of intersection of DR' and CR_1', DR' and CS_1', DS' and CR_1', DS' and CS_1' by U, X, Y, and Z, respectively. Finally, draw the pairs of lines UA and UA', XA and XA', YA and YA', ZA and ZA'. Each of these, taken by itself, will then satisfy the proposed problem. That is, every such line-pair touches a definite conic in the points A and A' under consideration, a conic which at the same time is tangent to the three given lines b, c, and d. Accordingly, the problem admits, in general, of four solutions, or there exist four conics which have the three given tangents, as well as the two given points in common. And so on.

The following additional double problems, which it may be noticed are partly combinations and partly special cases of the preceding problems (2 to 7), may be easily solved by means of them.

PROBLEM 8

Find the points of intersection of a given line and a conic of which (a) *four points and one tangent, or* (b) *four tangents and one point are given.*

PROBLEM 9

Find the lines which pass through a given point and are tangent to a conic of which (a) *four tangents and one point, or* (b) *four points and one tangent are given.*

PROBLEM 10

Find the points of intersection of a given line and a conic of which (a) *three points and two tangents, or* (b) *three tangents and two points are given.*

PROBLEM 11

Find the lines which pass through a given point and are tangent to a conic of which (a) *three tangents and two points, or* (b) *three points and two tangents are given.*

PROBLEM 12

Find the points of intersection of a given line and a conic given by (a) *four points and the tangent at one of them, or* (b) *four tangents and the point of contact of one of them.*

PROBLEM 13

Find the lines passing through a given point and tangent to a conic given by (a) *four tangents and the point of contact of one of them, or* (b) *four points and the tangent at one of them.*

PROBLEM 14

Find the points of intersection of a given line and a conic given by (a) *three points and the tangents at two of them, or* (b) *three tangents and the points of contact of two of them.*

PROBLEM 15

Find the lines passing through a given point and tangent to a conic given by (a) *three tangents and the points of contact of two of them, or* (b) *three points and the tangents at two of them.*

It may be seen that problems 8 and 9, for example, may be reduced to problems 2 and 3 by means of problems 4 and 5; and similarly, problems 10 and 11 may be reduced to problems 2 and 3 by means of problems 6 and 7, etc.; from which the number of solutions which may possibly belong to each of the present problems is easy to find.

PROBLEM 16

If two common (or intersection) points of two conics and any three special points of each are given, find their other two common points[69] *as well as their four common tangents.*

The conics may be denoted by k and k_1, their two given common points by R and S, the other three given points of the conic k by A, B, and C, and those of k_1 by A_1, B_1, and C_1, and the two desired common points by R' and S'. Then among the different methods of solution of the problem there is the following, for example.

Draw the lines AR and BS, CS; and seek the points A'' and B'', C'' in which they cut k_1 (besides in R and S) the second time—which we know can be easily done by means of the ruler alone, since five points of k_1 are given—; and forthwith draw the line-pairs AB and $A''B''$, AC and $A''C''$.   Call the points in which they intersect one another P and Q, respectively, and draw the line PQ.   Then this is a common secant (associated with the given RS) of the two conics k and k_1.   It is therefore only necessary further to find its intersections with one of the conics (2, a), to have the points R' and S' desired in the problem.

On the other hand, to find the four common tangents take any point P' (which, however, lies outside the conics) on the given secant RS, and draw from it to each conic two tangents.   Seek forthwith, by means of the ruler, their points of contact A_2 and B_2, A_2' and B_2', and then draw the line-pairs A_2A_2' and B_2B_2', A_2B_2' and B_2A_2', which intersect in the points E and I, respectively.   These are jointly the points of intersection of the desired two pairs of common tangents, which may then be found at once by problem 3.

A simpler solution of the problem under consideration I shall give and prove in another place.[70]

PROBLEM 17

If to two conics (k and k_1) two common tangents (a' and a_1') and also any three special tangents to each (as a, b, c and a_1, b_1, c_1) are given, find the other two common tangents of the conics and their four common points.

Let the points in which a' and a_1' are cut by a, b, c be A, B, C and A_1, B_1, C_1, respectively.   From each of the last three points draw to k_1 a second tangent (which, of course, exists besides a_1' already mentioned).   Denote the points in which they cut a' by A', B', C', respectively; and on the line a', by means of the auxiliary circle, forthwith seek the two points R' and S' for the three point-pairs A and A', B and B', C and C'.   Finally, draw from each of these points a (second) tangent to k (or k_1).   These will also be tangent to k_1 (or k) and are, consequently, the two desired common tangents.—The common points of the conics are found at once in a way corresponding to that used in the case of the common tangents in the previous example.

A host of further problems might be formulated, which would be put together from the last two (16 and 17) and the earlier problems, as, for example, the following.

PROBLEM 18

If two common points of two conics and also any three special tangents to each of them are given, find their other common points, as well as their common tangents.

PROBLEM 19

If two common tangents to two conics are given, and besides any three special points of each of them, find their other common tangents, as well as their common points. And so on.

As the above examples adequately show, all such problems are solved without the least difficulty, so that I do not consider it necessary to engage in the matter further. For, it is readily observed that, for example, problem 18 in general includes sixteen cases (because of the final remark in the solution of problem 7), each of which may be applied in particular to problem 16. Similarly with reference to problem 19.

Of problems concerning conics I shall here add only the following pair.

PROBLEM 20

In a conic given by any five points (or by any five conditions) describe a polygon of n sides, which is at the same time circumscribed about any given polygon of n sides (i. e., whose sides at the same time pass through n arbitrary given points in a definite order).

PROBLEM 21

Describe about a conic given by any five tangents a polygon of n sides, which is at the same time inscribed in any given polygon of n sides (i. e., whose vertices at the same time lie in order of any n given lines).

Of these two problems the first, or rather only a particular case of it, has acquired a rare distinction, since it has occupied the attention of the most famous mathematicians.[71] One process by which the problem may be solved with the auxiliary means here permitted consists chiefly in the following.

Let m_2 be the conic and n_2 the given polygon of n sides. By any three of the five given points of the conic, which may be called A_2, B_2, C_2, a circle is determined. Call it (M_1). First of all, by means of the auxiliary circle (M), the centers of similitude E and I of the circles (M) and (M_1) may now be found (for which we need no more then the three points of (M_1)). By means of E and I determine any two new points of the circle (M_1), as D_1 and E_1. Then there may be found a pole of perspective for (M_1) and m_2, since five points of each are given (in most cases the pole is the point of intersection of two common tangents to the conics). Call it P. By means of P and a common secant of (M_1) and m_2, as the secant A_2B_2, we find forthwith the polygon of n sides n_1 belonging to the circle (M_1), corresponding to the n-sided polygon n_2 regarded as belonging to the conic m_2. And then by means of E and I

there may easily be found, also, the n-sided polygon n', belonging to (M), which corresponds to the n-sided polygon n_1 belonging to (M_1). Thereupon, describe by means of the ruler alone in the given circle (M) an n-sided polygon n'', which is at the same time circumscribed about the given n-sided polyogon n'.[72]   Seek forthwith, by means of E and I, the n-sided polygon n_1'', belonging to the circle (M_1), corresponding to n'' with respect to the center of similitude E (or I).   Then (by means of P and A_2B_2) seek the n-sided polygon n_2'', belonging to the conic m_2, corresponding to n_1''.   This last will satisfy the demand of the problem.—In a corresponding way the other problem (21) may be solved.

NOTE: The preceding problems, from the second on, are, as may be noted, arranged in corresponding pairs according to the so-called principle of duality: namely, 2 and 3, 4 and 5, ... , 20 and 21.

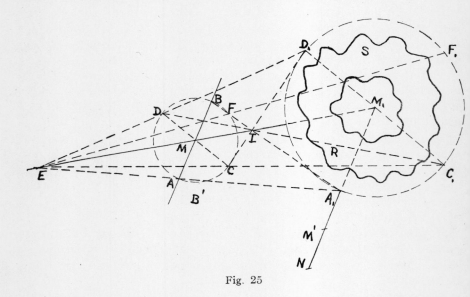

Fig. 25

PROBLEM 22

If any point A_1 (Fig. 25) of a circle and its center M_1 are given, the latter, however, being by hypothesis inaccessible, find other points of the circle at will.

Suppose, for example, that the point M_1 is given by some high object, as by a tower or tree, etc., standing on a little island or in the middle of a city, so that one cannot easily reach the same from all sides throughout the region RS, but indeed one can see it from the point A_1 and from other points $M, E, A, \ldots$. And suppose it is demanded to inclose the water RS surrounding the island, or the city by a circular street, canal, etc., which passes through the given point A_1 and in whose center stands the object M_1. Then *one man alone*, with few instruments to aid him, namely by means of rods and a chain (or cord) of a definite length, may find as follows many points at will through which the road, etc., mentioned passes.

At A_1 place a rod and in the direction M_1A_1, in which M_1 is visible, take any two equal segments, as $A_1M' = M'N$, and at M' and N also place rods. On a level place lay off a line AB which is parallel (§ 6, I) to $A_1M'N$. At the point M, which is taken as the center of the auxiliary circle, place a rod which is surrounded by a loose ring to which is fastened one end of the chain. Take $MA = MB =$ the length of the chain, and place rods at A and B. Now, further, place a rod at E where the lines A_1A and M_1M intersect, as well as at I where the lines A_1B and M_1M intersect. Then with the help of these preparations there may easily be found as many points of the circle (M_1) as are desired. For, stretch the chain in any direction, for example, as towards C. Here place another rod; and stretch the chain then in exactly the opposite direction, to D, and place another rod here. Then the intersections C_1 of the lines EC and DI, as well as D_1 of the lines ED and CI, are points of the circle (M_1).

If such obstacles existed that one could not see across the space R, then not from E and I to C_1, there would first of all be determined only the desired group of points along the visible arc A_1D_1; and then the auxiliary circle would be taken elsewhere to get a new arc or to lengthen the former one; and so the process would be carried on, until the circle (M_1) was complete.

If, instead of the center M_1 of the circle to be constructed and one point A_1 in its circumference, any three points of the circumference, as $A_1, D_1,$ and F_1, were given, then one way of solving the problem would be as follows.

Draw any triangle ADF, whose sides are parallel, respectively, to the sides of the given triangle $A_1D_1F_1$. Seek the center M of the circle ADF (i. e., of the circle circumscribed about the triangle ADF), as well as the centers of similitude E and I of the circles ADF and $A_1D_1F_1$; and then proceed exactly as above. Of course, to draw, for example, the line AD parallel to the line given by the two points A_1 and D_1 it is necessary to produce the latter past one of its end-points in order to be able to take two equal segments in this prolongation, as previously the segments $A_1M' = M'N$. This prolongation is, however, possible, as is well known, even in the case where neither is one of the two extremities A_1 and D_1 visible from the other, nor is the segment (from A_1 to D_1) existing between them accessible, but if only these same are visible from the side as from B'.[73] The same applies to the other two pairs of sides AF and A_1F_1, DF and D_1F_1. The similar triangles $A_1D_1F_1$ and ADF are then either *similarly situated* or *dissimilarly situated*. In the first case, which occurs in the present figure, the lines passing through corresponding vertices of the triangles (as the lines A_1A and D_1D) intersect in the *external* center of similitude E. And so on.

NOTES

1. Mascheroni's *"Gebrauch des Zirkels,"* translated from the Italian into French by CARETTE, and *from French* into German by GRÜSON, Berlin, 1825.

* There have been five editions of Mascheroni's work:

La Geometria del Compasso di LORENZO MASCHERONI. Paris, 1797. 266 p. + 14 plates. Nuova edizione, Palermo, 1901. 16 + 152 pp. (Figures in text. "Lorenzo Mascheroni e le sue opere matematiche" by G. FAZZARI, p. *iii–xiv*. In some copies the year 1903 is on a label pasted over the original date, 1901.)

Géométrie du Compas par L. Mascheroni: ouvrage traduite de l'Italien par A. M. Carette. À Paris, An VI (1798). 24 + 264 p. + 14 plates. Seconde édition. Paris, 1828. 16 + 328 p. + 14 plates.

L. Mascheroni's Gebrauch des Zirkels aus dem Italiänischen in's Französische übersetzt durch Herrn A. M. Carette. In's Deutsche übersetzt, vermehrt mit der Theorie vom Gebrauch des Proportionalzirkels und mit einer Sammlung zur Uebung von mehr denn 400 rein geometrischen Sätzen von J. P. Grüson. Berlin, 1825. 20 + 540 p. + 19 Kupfertafeln. (The translation occupies p. V–XX and 1–274.)*

* Three other books have been written on this subject, namely:

B. E. COUSINERY, *Géométrie Élémentaire du Compas exposant les divers Systèmes de Tracé que comprie l'emploi exclusif du Compas, tant les rigoureux que les approximatifs, pour de servir de prolégomènes au rapporteur de précision.* Paris, 1854, iv, 216 p. + 5 folding plates.

A. QUEMPER DE LANASCOL, *Géométrie du Compas.* Paris, 1925, xx, 406 p.

GEORG MOHR, *Euclides Danicus.* Amsterdam, 1672, 36 p. This work was generally unknown till it was reprinted in facsimile, with a German translation and an introduction, by the Danish Society of Sciences (Copenhagen, 1928, 8, 2, 36, 4, 41 p. + 3 folding plates). Compasses only are used in constructions. Thus MOHR in such discussion preceded MASCHERONI by 125 years.

Four additional references to this extensive literature may be given. (a) A. ADLER, *Theorie der Geometrischen Konstruktionen.* Leipzig, 1906, p. 92–122. (b) A. CAYLEY, "On Mascheroni's geometry of the compass," *Messenger of Mathematics*, v. 14, 1885, p. 179–181. (c) E. W. HOBSON, "On geometrical constructions by means of the compass," [presidential address before the Mathematical Association, London], *Mathematical Gazette*, v. 7, 1913, p. 49–54. (d) H. P. HUDSON, *Ruler & Compasses.* London, 1916, p. 131–143.*

2. *For example: F. J. SERVOIS, *Solutions peu connus de différens problèmes de géométrie pratique pour servir de supplément aux traités connus de cette science.* À Metz, An XII [1804], 79, 28, 3 p. + plate of figures.

J. V. PONCELET, "Reflexions sur l'usage de l'analyse algébrique dans la géométrie suivies de la solution de quelques problèmes dépendant de la géométrie de la règle," *Annales de mathématiques* (GERGONNE), v. 8, p. 141–155, 1817.

C. J. BRIANCHON, *Application de la théorie des transversales.* Paris, 1818, vi, 62 p. + plate of figures.*

3. *STEINER has stated this last clause carelessly; it should read: "provided that some fixed auxiliary circle and its center are given in the plane."

"Conjecture" (Vermuthung) does not adequately describe the results already obtained in this connection by PONCELET, at least. See Section II of the "Editor's Introduction."*

4. *Hereafter *line* used alone means *straight line*.*

5. *Here, and in what follows, STEINER does not distinguish between the terms *line* and *line-segment*.*

6. *In the preface to his work *La Geometria del Compasso*.*

7. *This memoir of STEINER was published in 1826 and occupied pages 161–184 and 252–288 of CRELLE's *Journal*, v. 1. It has been twice reprinted: (1) in STEINER's *Gesammelte Werke*, v. 1, Berlin, 1881, p. 17–76, edited by KIEPERT; and (2) in OSTWALD's *Klassiker der exacten Wissenschaften* as no. 123, edited with notes by R. STURM, Leipzig, 1901.

The first part of *Systematische Entwickelung* was first published, in book form, at Berlin in 1832. It has been twice reprinted: (1) in STEINER's *Gesammelte Werke*. v. 1, Berlin, 1881, p. 229–460, edited by SCHRÖTER; (2) in Ostwald's *Klassiker*, etc., as no. 82–83, edited with notes by A. J. VON OETTINGEN, Leipzig, 1896.*

8. *The last clause should read: "when any fixed auxiliary circle and its center are given."*

9. *Named "harmonicales" by P. DE LA HIRE (*Traité des Sections Coniques*, Paris, 1685, p. 5f.) and "faisceau harmonique" (harmonic pencil) by C. J. BRIANCHON (*Mémoire sur les lignes du second ordre*. Paris, 1817, p. 9).*

10. *It was L. N. CARNOT (*Essai sur la Théorie des Transversales*. Paris, 1806, p. 69) who bestowed the name complete quadrilateral on a system of four coplanar straight lines no three of which are concurrent.*

11. This statement is rather too brief; a more adequate one occurs at the end of the paragraph.

12. *That is, *GD;* as *d* referred to *FD.**

13. *This is a fundamental theorem of projective geometry concerning harmonic ranges and pencils.*

14. *This construction is given by P. DE LA HIRE, *Sectiones Conicae*. Paris, 1685, p. 9, prop. 20.*

15. *If *A*, *M*, and *I* were *any* three points on *a*, and *H*, *L*, and *C* any three points on *c*, then the points (AL, HM), (AC, HI), (MC, LI) are collinear. This was a result probably known to EUCLID (300 B.C.) and is proved in PAPPUS (*c.* 300 A.D.), *Collection*, Bk. VII, prop. 143 (v. 2, ed. by F. HULTSCH). It is the special case of the "mystic hexagram" theorem of PASCAL (1640) when the conic is a pair of straight lines, *a* and *c*.*

16. *This problem may be regarded as a particular case of § 5, VI, as it is there noted.*

17. *STEINER had here $CE:ED=DB:CB$. This was corrected in the other German editions.*

17a. *The discussion in this paragraph is notably ingenious.*

18. *The problem, "Given a parallelogram, construct with ruler only a parallel to a given line," goes back to the time of W. J. s' GRAVESANDE (d. 1742) at least (see his *Oeuvres philosophiques*, Amsterdam, 1774, part 1, p. 174). It is also discussed by J. H. LAMBERT (in his *Freye Perspective oder Anweisung*. 2 ed., Zürich, 1774, v. 2, p. 169), and by PONCELET (*Traité des propriétés projectives des figures*. Paris, 1822, p. 106–107; and *Applications d'analyse et de géométrie*. Paris, 1862, p. 437–439 [this part of the work was written in 1813–14 by PONCELET when he was in prison]). See also L. CREMONA, *Elements of Projective Geometry*, translated from the Italian by C. Leudesdorf. Oxford, 1885, p. 96–97; G. DE LONGCHAMPS, *Essai sur la géométrie de la règle et de l'équerre*. Paris, 1890, p. 232–235; *Mathematical Questions and Solutions from the "Educational Times*," v. 57, 1892, p. 88; J. W. RUSSELL, *An Elementary Treatise on Pure Geometry*, new and revised ed., Oxford, 1905, p. 318; M. I. TRACHTENBERG, *Mathematical Gazette*, v. 4, 1908, p. 334; and J. M. CHILD, *Mathematical Gazette*, v. 5, 1910, p. 283–284.*

19. *The statement here is loose; later in the paragraph it appears that "any given rational ratio" is meant.*

20. *STEINER had (§ 6, II) here. This slip is uncorrected in the other German editions.*

21. Although these properties are of little service for the chief purpose of this book (third chapter), nevertheless they are briefly developed here, since they are interesting in and for themselves, are still almost entirely missing from textbooks, and may easily be derived in an elementary manner from preceding considerations.

22. *Although in Fig. 12 *d* is drawn as a half-line from *B'*, it is evidently intended here that we should consider the angle which *B'A* makes with *DB'* produced.*

23. *The converse of bk. III, prop. 32, of EUCLID's *Elements* is here assumed, namely: "If a straight line drawn through one extremity of a chord of a circle make with that chord angles equal respectively to the angles in the alternate segments of the circle, the straight line so drawn touches the circle." PAPPUS assumes the consequence of this proposition in one place (*Collection*, ed. HULTSCH, p. 196; see also p. 826).*

24. *We have translated "harmonische Pol" by "pole," a term introduced by SERVOIS, *Annales de Mathématiques Pures et Appliquées*, v. 1, p. 337, 1811.*

25. *Here and in what follows the ordinary word "polar" has been employed as an equivalent for STEINER's word "Harmonische." The term polar is due to J. D. GERGONNE, *Annales de Mathématiques Pures et Appliquées*, v. 3, 1812, p. 297,; on p. 301 he first employed the terms "pole" and "polar plane" in connection with surfaces of the second order.*

26. *Again too brief a statement to be intelligible independent of the context. Compare Note 11.*

27. *In the original FI was here; this has been corrected in the other German editions.*

28. *This construction for the polar of a point with respect to a circle (or any conic), with emphasis on the fact that the construction can be carried through with ruler alone, is given in the article of SERVOIS, 1811, referred to above, Note 24.*

29. *This result is given by P. DE LA HIRE in his *Sectiones Conicae*. Paris, 1685, bk. I, props. 26–28; it is generalized to conic sections, book 2, props. 23–27.*

30. *This construction requiring ruler only, was given by WOLDECK WELAND in his *Strena Mathematica sive Elegantiorum Problemata Triga*. Leiden, 1640.*

31. *A. J. VON OETTINGEN's edition, Zweiter Theil, p. 28–34.*

32. *The theory of polar reciprocation or duality of figures was developed in the early years of the nineteenth century. One of the very first applications of the theory was the derivation by BRIANCHON (*Journal de l'École Polytechnique*, v. 6, 1806, p. 301) of his famous theorem as the dual of PASCAL's hexagram proposition for a conic (compare Note 15). PONCELET seemed to be the first to enunciate the result that by the principle of polar reciprocation as a point traces out one curve the polars of the points envelop another curve (*Annales de Mathématiques Pures et Appliquées*, v. 8, p. 209 f., 1818; see also PONCELET's *Applications d'Analyse*. v. 2, 1864, p. 476–503). The general subject is discussed by PONCELET in a memoir in CRELLE's *Journal*, v. 4, 1829. For historical details see E. KÖTTER, *Die Entwickelung der synthetischen Geometrie*. Leipzig, 1901, p. 50–51 (also in *Jahresbericht d. deutschen Mathematiker-Vereinigung*, v. 5); and CHASLES, *Aperçu Historique sur l'Origine et le Développement des Méthodes en Géométrie*. 1837, p. 370–371.*

33. *The e in the original lacks the subscript. This misprint has been rectified in the other German editions.*

34. *I = internal, E = external. The original had I = inner, A = äusser.*

35. *Not necessarily on the circumference (M_1).*

36. *At this point the attempt to continue modifying STEINER's notation so as to indicate the plane in which a point is being considered will have to be given up.*

37. *Here and in the theorem which follows, some such words as "central line" would be more accurate than STEINER's term, "diameter"; the points P_2 and Q_2 may fall outside of the circle (M_2).*

38. *That the medians of a triangle are concurrent and trisect one another at its center of gravity was undoubtedly known to ARCHIMEDES (*Opera*, ed. HEIBERG, 2 ed., v. 2, p. 160, 1. 13–15, and p. 272–275; v. 3, p. 276–277, commentary of EUTOCIUS); but the result was first explicitly formulated by HERON of Alexandria (*Opera*, ed. NIX and SCHMIDT, v. 2, fasc. 1, p. 188–191).

*Commentary of PROCLUS indicates (ed. FRIEDLEIN, p. 72, 1. 17–19) that the theorem regarding the concurrence (at the "ortho-center") of the altitudes of a triangle was probably known to EUCLID but purposely excluded from his *Elements*. The fifth proposition in a *Book of Lemmas*, ascribed by Arabians to ARCHIMEDES, contains what is equivalent to the theorem; see T. L. HEATH, *The Works of Archimedes*. Cambridge, 1897, p. 305–307.

*That the perpendicular bisectors of the sides of a triangle meet in the center of its circumscribed circle is an immediate consequence of the first proposition of the third book of EUCLID's *Elements*.

*EULER showed that the center of gravity, the orthocenter, and the circumcenter of a triangle are collinear, "Euler's line" (*Novi Commen. Acad. Se. Petr.*, v. 11 (1765), 1767, p. 103–123; an abstract of this paper by J. S. MACKAY is given in *Proc. Edinb. Math. So.*, v. 4, 1886, p. 51–55). EULER showed also that the distance of the center of gravity to the circumcenter was one-half its distance to the orthocenter.

*In a memoir by BRIANCHON and PONCELET published in January, 1821 (*Annales de Math.*, v. 11), occurs the following theorem (p. 215) regarding the nine-point circle: "The circle which passes through the feet of the perpendiculars dropped from the vertices of a triangle on the opposite sides, passes also through the middle points of these sides, and the middle points of the distances of the vertices from the point of intersection of the altitudes." It is also shown that this circle is the locus of the centers of all rectangular hyperbolas described through the vertices, and therefore through the orthocenter, of the triangle. That this circle is tangent to the inscribed circle and the three escribed circles of the triangle was proved by K. W. FEUERBACH, *Eigenschaften einiger merkwürdiger Punkte des geradlinigen*

Dreiecks. Nürnberg, 1822, § 57; in second ed., Haarlem, 1908, p. 45. This is "Feuerbach's theorem." FEUERBACH shows also that the center of the nine-point circle is on EULER's line, and equally distant from the circumcenter and orthocenter.

*The "Herr Prof. DOVE" referred to by STEINER is undoubtedly H. W. DOVE (1803–1879), his colleague at the Gewerbschule in Berlin at the time this book appeared, and later the distinguished meteorologist. Where DOVE may have published the theorems to which STEINER refers, we have been unable to determine.

*That rectangular hyperbola through the vertices of a triangle and its orthocenter, which passes also through its center of gravity, is called KIEPERT's hyperbola (*Nouvelles Annales de Mathématiques*, 1869, p. 40–42), or "the nine-point hyperbola" (BROCARD, *Journal de Mathématiques Spéciales*, v. 4–5, 1884–1885), which is of importance in the geometry of the triangle.*

39.   *In the edition we are translating Figs. 16 and 17 are interchanged.*

40.   *This result, for circles exterior to one another, was given by MONGE in his *Géométrie Descriptive*, Paris, 1798, p. 54–55, and he states that it is only a particular case of a more general result for any four spheres in space and the vertices of various tangent cones lying by sixes on five planes; there were really eight such planes, MONGE overlooked three. Discussion of this result, and of the beginnings of the study of centers of similitude of circles is taken up in articles by R. C. ARCHIBALD in *Amer. Mathem. Mo.*, v. 22, 1915, p. 6–12, v. 23, 1916, p. 159–161. The conclusion reached is, that the theorem of our text was known to APOLLONIUS of Perga. The term "center of similitude" is due to EULER: "De centro similitudinis," *Nova Acta acad. sc. Petrop.*, v. 9 (1791), 1795, p. 154—"conventuri exhib. die 23 Octob. 1777." Attention may also be drawn to B. H. BROWN, "Centers of similitude and their N-dimensional analogies," *Amer. Mathem. Mo.*, v. 23, p. 155–159.

41.   *This result is in effect stated incidentally in the anonymous little booklet by T. PERELLI, *Soluzione d'Alcuni Problemi Geometrici esposta nell'articolo primo del Tomo VII. Parte I. del Giornale Letterario di Firenze* [1755, col. 529], Florence, 1755, p. 22–24. The case of a circle tangent to two others externally is to be found in PAPPUS, *Collection*, ed. HULTSCH, p. 208–211.*

42.   *In STEINER's *Allgemeine Theorie über das Berühren und Schneiden der Kreise und der Kugeln* (Zürich and Leipzig, 1931), written in the years 1823–26, there is a section (p. 26–55) on "Power and the locus of points of equal power with respect to coplanar circles."*

43.   *This was 16 in the original.*

44.   *All German editions, except that of WEIERSTRASS, have QM_2 here instead of QM^2.*

45.   *In the *Plane Loci* of APOLLONIUS (225 B.C.) the following result is proved (PAPPUS, *Collection*, ed. HULTSCH, p. 854–855):

$$NM^2 - NM_1^2 = 2MM_1 \cdot PQ,$$

where P is the middle point of MM_1.*

46.   *In EUCLID's *Elements*, bk. III, props. 35, 36, it is shown that if through a point inside, or outside, a circle any two secants are drawn the rectangles contained by the segments of these secants are equal. It is this product of the segments which STEINER defined as the "power of the point with respect to the circle" (*Journal für die reine u. angew. Math.*, v. 1, 1826, p. 164). For English, American, and French readers a more familiar term for line of equal powers is "radical axis," a term introduced by L. GAULTIER (*Journ. de l'École Polyt.*, v. 9, cahier 16, 1813, p. 139).

*The locus of points from which tangents of equal length can be drawn to two conics is a curve of the twentieth degree (*L'Intermédiaire des Mathématiciens*, v. 18, 1911, p. 193–194, v. 19, 1912, p. 261–262). LAGUERRE and D'OCAGNE considered the more general problem of the locus of points from which equal tangents could be drawn to two curves S and S', under certain suppositions (*Bulletin de la Société Mathém. de France*, v. 3, 1875, p. 46, v. 5, 1877, p. 25–26; *Oeuvres de Laguerre.* v. 2, 1905, p. 450–451; *Nouv. Annales de Mathématiques*, v. 70, 1911, p. 93, 475–477).*

47.   *It was GAULTIER also who gave (*l. c.*, Note 46, p. 143) the name "radical center" to the "point of equal powers" for three circles.*

48.   *The usual designation of such points is "inverse points," with respect to the center of inversion E, and with power of inversion which is here called the joint power of the circles (M) and (M_1). These same ideas were developed earlier by STEINER in a publication of 1826 ("Einige geometrische Betrachtungen," *Gesammelte Werke*, v. 1, p. 32–33). But it was not until 1913 that one could be sure that STEINER at this time, or earlier, had clear ideas

about inversion as a geometrical transformation. F. Bützberger showed (*Über bizentrische Polygone, Steinersche Kreis- und Kugelreihen und die Erfindung der Inversion*. Leipzig, 1913) the existence of a Steiner document dated 1824 in which the theory was definitely developed under the picturesque heading "Von der Wiedergeburt und der Auferstehung" (On Rebirth and Resurrection).

*Before 1840 two other writers have been mentioned as having written about inversion. The first of these is L. I. Magnus, (*a*) "Nouvelle méthode pour decouvrir des théorèmes de géométrie," *Journal f. d. reine und angew. Mathematik*, v. 8, 1832, p. 51–63; (*b*) "Quelques théorèmes de géométrie," *idem*, v. 9, 1832, p. 135–138; (*c*) *Sammlung von Aufgaben und Lehrsätzen aus der analytischen Geometrie der Ebene*, Berlin, 1833, p. 229–236, 290–292). The second is G. Bellavitis, "Teoria delle figure inverse e loro uso nella geometria elementare," *Annali delle Scienze del regno Lombardo-Veneto*, v. 6, 1836, p. 126–141. But there was an earlier writer of importance whose paper has been entirely overlooked. I refer to the beautiful memoir of A. Quetelet, "Résumé d'une nouvelle théorie des caustiques," Acad. royale d. Sci....de Belgique, *Nouveaux Mémoires*, v. 4, 1827, p. 81–113. This memoir was presented to the Academy Nov. 5, 1825. Hence its contents may well have been worked out as early as 1824. The author uses the term "inversion" to characterize the transformation which he employs and he derives the necessary formulae in rectangular and polar coordinates. The cissoid is noted as an inverse of the parabola and the limaçon as the inverse of a conic with respect to its focus. The theory is applied to caustics.

*Hence the name inversion and the earliest elaborate publication on the subject are due to Quetelet. Moreover Quetelet's conception of the subject may well have been just as early as Steiner's.

*It will be of interest to add that already about 225 B.C. Apollonius of Perga in his book on *Plane Loci* proved that the inverse of a circle is a circle. This is prop. XVII, bk. I, in Robert Simson's restoration. *Apollonii Pergaei Locorum Planorum Liber II*. Glasgow, 1749; and in J. W. Camerer's German translation of this, Leipzig, 1796. The proposition is part of a more general one in Pappus, *Collection*, ed. F. Hultsch, v. 2, Berlin, 1877, p. 663–665; or in Ver Eecke's French translation, Bruges, 1932, v. 2, p. 496. In effect, the Simson reduction of the proposition is the following: lines $r_1(AA')$, $r_2(BB')$, making a constant angle with one another, are drawn from the two given points A and B, and $r_1r_2 = k^2$, a constant; if A' describes a circle, so does B'.*

49. *A simpler construction is given by F. Redl, *L'Enseignement Mathématique*, v. 12, 1910, p. 309–310. See also H. P. Hudson, *Ruler & Compasses*. London, 1916, p. 118–121.*

50. *This is a problem solved by Lambert in his *Freye Perspective*. Zürich, v. 2, 1774, p. 171–172; and *Johann Heinrich Lambert, Schriften zur Perspektive* ed. by Max Steck. Berlin, 1943, p. 375. His enunciation of the problem is as follows: "Given a circle with its middle point, with ruler only drop a perpendicular on a given line".*

51. *Because S is the pole of PP_1 which must be perpendicular to SM (§ 10, I).*

52. *The first and Oettingen's editions here give Ω instead of $\mathfrak{P}_1$; the Schröter edition has $\mathfrak{PP}_1$ (oder $\Omega\Omega_1$), that is, in our notation PP_1 (or QQ_1).*

53. *Euclid's *Elements*, bk. I, prop. 23, is a solution of this problem with ruler and compasses.*

54. *Given a circle and its center, Lambert solves this problem with ruler only in his *Freye Perspective*. Zürich, v. 2, 1774, p. 177; 1943 ed. p. 378.*

55. *Problem four might be used to apply to M_1C_1 at M_1 an angle equal to the angle $A_1M_1C_1$; this would give an angle twice as large as the angle $A_1M_1C_1$. This process might be continued to multiply the angle at will.*

56. To find the points E_1 and I_1 we can also, because of the above preliminaries, instead of drawing through E_2 the line E_2E_1, pass through I_2 the line I_2I_1 parallel to M_2M_1; where the point I is obtained at once by the line E_2I_1, and the point E_1 by the line II_2. Or thirdly, the midpoint I of the line M_1M_2 can first be sought (second problem), and then by means of the lines II_2 and IE_2 the points E_1 and I_1 can be found.

57. *If only one segment is wanted the problem may be solved very briefly as follows: Join A_1M_2; through M_1 draw $M_1B_2 \parallel A_1M_2$ and meeting $M_2B_2 \parallel A_1M_1$ in B_2.*

58. *The first and Oettingen's editions here give ε instead of $\mathfrak{e}$.*

59. *Indicated in Fig. 23 of the original edition and of Schröter's but not in Oettingen's edition.*

60. *Here, in problem seven, and elsewhere in this book, geometrical problems involving obstacles or unfavorable positions of lines are considered. In recent times three separate

publications have dealt with such problems. They are: A. WITTING, *Geometrische Konstruktionen insbesondere in begrenzter Ebene.* Progr., Dresden, 1899; and P. Zühlke, (a) *Ausführung elementargeometrische Konstruktionen bei ungünstigen Lagerverhältnissen.* Leipzig, 1906; (b) *Konstruktionen in begrenzter Ebene.* Leipzig, 1913. second ed. 1932; Among older works containing such problems are: F. VAN SCHOOTEN, *Exercitationum mathematicarum libri quinque.* Leyden, 1657 (Dutch edition, 1658); J. H. LAMBERT, *Freye Perspective.* 2 ed., Zürich, 1774, v. 2; L. MASCHERONI, *Problemi per gli agrimensori.* Pavia, 1793 (French ed. Paris, 1803; third Italian ed. with the title *Problemi di geometria*, by SACCHI, Milan, 1832); F. J. SERVOIS, *Solutions peu connues de différens problèmes de géométrie pratique.* Metz, 1804; and C. J. BRIANCHON, *Application de la Théorie des Transversales.* Paris, 1818. References may be given also to F. REDL, "Construction de planimétrie. Solutions nouvelles de problèmes compliqués par des conditions particulière," *L'Enseignement Mathématique,* v. 12, 1910, p. 293–308; and to A. BARUCH, "Die verschiedenen Methoden zur Lösung von Aufgaben der darstellenden Geometrie bei ungünstigen Lagenverhält, nissen," *Zeitschrift für mathem. u. naturw. Unterricht,* v. 53, 1922, p. 126–133, 161–168.*

61. I need here, for example, to recall simply the earlier construction of a circle tangent to three given circles. And that even in the usual school instruction similar examples present themselves in the case of much simpler problems every observant teacher may be easily convinced.

*The problem referred to in the first sentence of the previous paragraph was the main problem in a work by APOLLONIUS of Perga (about 225 B.C.) called "On Contacts" or "On Tangencies." While the text of this work has not come down to us we have an account of it by PAPPUS in his *Collection* (ed. HULTSCH, v. 2, 1877, p. 644–649, 821–853). This account has been the basis of numerous restorations (for example, VIETA, 1600; GHETALDUS, 1607, translated into English by LAWSON, 1764, second ed. 1771; CAMERER, 1795, containing also a reprint of VIETA, 1600; VIETH's edition of VIETA, 1820; CHRISTMANN, 1821) but in not one of them is any use made of lemma 117 which PAPPUS gives as used by APOLLONIUS in the second book of his work. The enunciation of this lemma or problem may be paraphrased as follows: Inscribe in a given circle a triangle whose sides or sides produced shall pass through three given collinear points. An appropriate setting for this problem was discovered by ROBERT SIMSON in 1734 (see R. SIMSON, *Opera Quaedam Reliqua.* Glasgow, 1776, Appendix, p. 20–23; for an English translation see *The Mathematician,* v. 3, 1848, p. 78) for solving the problem of describing a circle through a point tangent to two given circles. With very similar reasoning, however, his method might have been extended to the case of a circle tangent to three given circles. Doubtless independent of SIMSON this appears to have been first achieved by SCORZA in 1819 *Atti della reale Accad. d. Sc. e belle Lettere,* v. 1, p. 77–78. In notes for problems 20 and 21, we shall have occasion to return to lemma 117.*

62. *It is in connection with this passage that ADALBERT GRÜTTNER asserts (*Die Grundlagen der Geometrographie.* Leipzig, 1912, p. 8) that Steiner "has bounded the entire realm of geometrography. The first to approach the problem *systematically* was certainly Herr *Lemoine,* who assigns the year 1888 as the period for the beginning of geometrographic investigation." (É. LEMOINE, *Géométrographie ou art des constructions géométriques.* Paris, 1902, p. 8.)*

*After quoting from this same paragraph by STEINER, in a review (in *Jahrbuch über die Fortschritte der Mathematik,* v. 24, 1892, p. 524) of an earlier paper on geometrography by LEMOINE, LANGE remarks: "The treatise considered appears to the reviewer a highly satisfactory completion of the program drawn up sixty years ago by our old master."*

63. *In this Appendix are 22 problems, of which 21 are projective, not metrical, and the principle of duality is emphasized.*

64. *STEINER planned to issue five parts of this work; the first part appeared in 1832 (the present work was published in 1833). Compare Note 7 and the "Editor's Introduction" to the present edition.*

65. *This is evidently a very particular case of the following problem solved by SERVOIS, and others (*Annales de Mathématiques,* v. 2, 1811–12, p. 116; see also PONCELET, *Traité des propriétés projectives des figures.* Paris, 1822, p. 345): To construct a polygon whose vertices shall lie on given straight lines (each on each), and whose sides shall pass through given points (each through each). On page 115 of the *Annales,* LHUILIER gives a solution for the special case of triangles. Both SERVOIS and PONCELET drew particular attention to the special cases of the general problem which could be solved by the use of the ruler only.*

*In 1733 W. BRAIKENRIDGE published the following result, in effect, in his *Exercitatio Geometrica de Descriptione Linearum Curvarum* (London, 1733): If the sides of a polygon are restricted to pass through fixed points while all the vertices but one lie on fixed straight lines, the free vertex describes a conic section or a straight line. Since MACLAURIN claimed in a letter to JOHN MACHIN (*Philosophical Transactions*, v. 39, 1735, p. 143–165) that he had printed this result, but not published it, in 1721, it is usually known as the BRAIKENRIDGE-MACLAURIN theorem. (See C. TWEEDIE "The Braikenridge-Maclaurin theorem," *Mathematical Gazette*, v. 8, 1915, p. 142–144). From this result we may infer at once that there are, in general, two solutions of STEINER's problem 1 as first discussed, or as later generalized.*

66. *The problem of determining other points on a conic when five of its points are given, was solved by PAPPUS (about 300, in his *Collection*, ed. by HULTSCH, v. 3, p. 1077 f.). ZEUTHEN sets forth how APOLLONIUS of Perga (about 225 B.C.) had at his disposal means for determining a conic equivalent to stating that a conic is determined by five of its points (H. G. ZEUTHEN, *Die Lehre von den Kegelschnitten im Altertum*. Copenhagen, 1886, section 9). NEWTON proved, in effect, that a conic is uniquely determined by five points (*Principia*, 1687, bk. 1, lemma 18) and solved also the problems (*Principia*, bk. 1, props. 23–27) of finding points on a conic for which are given: (a) four points and one tangent; (b) three points and two tangents; (c) two points and three tangents: (d) one point and four tangents; (e) five tangents. These problems were also discussed by BRIANCHON in: (a) *Correspondance sur l'École Imp. Polytechnique*, v. 1, no. 10, April, 1808, p. 435; and (b) *Mémoire sur les lignes du second ordre*. Paris, 1817, paragraphs 39, 40, 45, 51, 55, and 59. Compare STEINER's problems 2–14. See also NEWTON, *Arithmetica Universalis*, 1707, p. 211–221. A recent convenient English edition of NEWTON's *Principia* is that edited by the late F. CAJORI, and published by the University of California, Berkeley, 1934. See also F. S. MACAULAY, "The conic determined by five points," *Mathematical Gazette*, v. 1, 1896, p. 12–14; and A. C. DIXON, "The conic through five given points," *Mathematical Gazette*, v. 4, 1908, p. 228–230.*

67. *Compare, for example, L. CREMONA, *Elements of Projective Geometry*. Oxford, 1885, p. 176–177, 179–180.*

68. Compare *Mémoire sur les Lignes du Second Ordre*. Paris, 1817, p. 47 by BRIANCHON, capitaine d'Artillerie, ancien élève de l'École Polytechnique; and *Abhängigkeit geometrischer Gestalten von einander*, part I, p. 285.

69. *Compare CREMONA, *Elements of Projective Geometry*. Oxford, 1885, p. 189.*

70. *We have not been able to locate this place.*

71. See KLÜGEL's *Mathematisches Wörterbuch*. Th. III, article "Kreis" § 115, S. 155, and especially the later papers on the same subject by the mathematicians GERGONNE, ENCONTRE, SERVOIS, ROCHAT, BRIANCHON, PONCELET, LHUILIER, etc., in *Annales de Mathématiques*, volumes I and VIII, in the *Journal de l'École Polytechnique*, cahier X, etc.
*The history of problems 20 and 21 begins with the lemma used by APOLLONIUS of Perga in the second book of his work "On Contacts," and already paraphrased in our Note 61 as follows: Inscribe in a given circle a triangle whose sides or sides produced shall pass through three given collinear points. The first generalization of this result was made in 1731 by ROBERT SIMSON (W. TRAIL, *Life and Writings of Robert Simson*. London, 1812, p. 97–98) who removed the condition for the collinearity of the given points. In 1776 CASTILLON presented an elegant geometrical solution with a discussion of various cases to the Berlin Academy (*Nouv. Mémoires*, 1779, p. 265 f.); the problem had been proposed to him by CRAMER in 1742. The day after CASTILLON read his paper before the Academy LAGRANGE handed him a trigonometrical solution of the problem "apparently for the purpose of showing that an analyst could solve in a single evening a problem that had confessedly required from a geometer of no mean powers many years of study." EULER and FUSS discussed the problem, and LEXELL at the request of EULER undertook to attempt the construction of LAGRANGE's result (*Acta. Acad. Sc. Petrop.*, part I, 1783, p. 91 f.; part II, 1784, p. 70 f.). Up to this time no method had been found which could be generalized to any polygon. This was discovered in 1784 by A. GIORDANO DI OTTAJANO when a student at Naples, and only 16 years of age. Hence the problem has been referred to as OTTAJANO's problem, although Ottajano was the name of the little village near to Vesuvius where GIORDANO was born. This solution as well as one contributed by request by MALFATTI, then professor of mathematics at Ferrara, were published in 1788 (*Memorie di matem. e fisica d. Soc. Ital.*, Verona).
*The SIMSON generalization for the triangle case was proposed as a problem in *Mathematical Repository*, v. 2, 1798, p. 60 and in the solution by WILLIAM WALLACE (p. 189–196) the impossibility of solving the problem for certain positions of the given points was noted for the first time. The dual of SIMSON's generalization, proposed for solution by GERGONNE

as question 1 of the first number of his *Annales des Mathématiques* (1810, p. 17), was as follows: "A circle and three lines in the same plane with it being given, it is required to circumscribe a triangle about the circle whose three vertices shall be upon the three given lines." Encontre showed (p. 122–124) that by the theory of poles and polars not only this problem but the corresponding general one regarding a polygon of m sides circumscribing a circle can be reduced to the solution of another problem [the one solved by Giordano] whose solution had been known for a long time. On page 259 Gergonne proposed to solve with ruler *only* the case when $m = 3$ and any conic is substituted for a circle; solutions by Rochat and Servois are given on pages 336–342. The general problems:

I. Inscribe in a given conic a polygon whose m sides, or sides produced, shall pass in order through m given points; and

II. Circumscribe about a given conic a polygon of m sides whose vertices shall lie in order on m given lines;

were considered and solved by Poncelet in 1817 (*Annales de Mathématiques*, v. 8, p. 151 f.). Poncelet notes also that if the m points in I are collinear, and the m lines in II are concurrent, these problems can be solved with ruler only.

*The next generalization was the inscription in a quadric surface of a gauche polygon of m sides passing in order through m points, first discussed by Sir William R. Hamilton (*Proc. Royal Irish Acad.*, v. 4, 1849–50; *Phil. Mag.*, s. 3, v. 35–36, 1849–50; *Lectures on Quaternions.* Dublin, 1853, p. 673–682, 701–730). Hamilton considered the solutions which depended on linear equations in finite differences as an especially tough piece of work (cf. *Life by* Graves, v. 3, 1889, p. 88, 426.). Later simplifications and extensions of Hamilton's discussions were given by M. Gardiner (*Quarterly Jl. Mathem.*, v. 7, 1866, p. 284–301; *Proc. Lond. Math. Soc.*, v. 2, 1867, p. 63–66; *New South Wales Royal Soc. Trans.*, v. 3, 1869, p. 38–41) and by Townsend (*Proc. London Math. Soc.*, v. 2, 1867, p. 21–24.)

*The best historical sketches of the problem are the following: T. S. Davies, "Historical notes on an ancient problem," *The Mathematician*, v. 3, 1848–50; E. Kötter, *Die Entwickelung der synthetischen Geometrie.* Leipzig, 1901, p. 143–149; J. M. Brückner, *Das Ottajanosche Problem—eine math. histor. Studie.* Zwickau, 1892; F. Dingeldey, *Encyclopédie des Sciences Mathématiques*, tome 3, v. 3, fasc. 1, 1911, p. 102–103.*

72. This is done, for example, by the process which Poncelet first made known in *Annales de Mathématiques*, v. 8.

73. See Crelle, *Handbuch des Feldmessens und Nivellirens.* Berlin, 1826, § 67, p. 116, where this problem among others is treated with insight.

INDEX

(Numbers refer to pages. Such a symbol as n51 refers to the corresponding number of a Note. The index is mainly for names.)

86

CORRIGENDA

P. 5, line −14, −15, *for* Preussis -cher, *read* Preussi-scher

P. 8, line − 5, *for* Utzenstorf, *read* Utzensdorf

P. 9, line 13, *for* einen, *read* einem
line 22, *for* Eléméntaires, *read* Élémentaires

P. 11, line 6, *for* tent then are, *read* tent they are
line −15, *for* Entwickelung, *read* Entwicklung

P. 14, line −15, *for* arbitary, *read* arbitrary

P. 20, line 12, *for* n-tuplye, *read* n-tuple

P. 23, line 17, *for* lead at, *read* lead, at

P. 37, line 15, *for* on, *read* no

P. 38, line −5, *for* manner,, *read* manner

P. 43, line 21, *for* and are half, *read* and half
line 37, *for* belongs, *read* belong

P. 44, line −6, *for* $E_2I_2I_3$, *read* $E_2I_3I_1$

P. 49, line 10, *for* pairs always, *read* pairs, always
line 12, *for* pairs their, *read* pairs, their

P. 51, line −2, *for* intersections, *read* intersecting

P. 64, line 10, *for* in narrow sense, *read* in the narrow sense
line 23, *for* matter in making, *read* matter of making

P. 68, line 5, *for* the lineä, *read* the line á

P. 73, line 22, *for* order of any, *read* order on any
line −9, *for* then, *read* than

P. 74, line 5, *for* polyogon, *read* polygon